Stepping Closer

Stories and Prayers

by Hilary Faith Jones

Published, edited and distributed by TLM Trading Limited
www.tlmtrading.com

First Published 2011

Design and editorial by Creative Plus Publishing Ltd
www.creative-plus.co.uk

Printed and bound in China by Imago

ISBN 978-0-902731-88-2

With thanks to our photographers:

Virginia Duhanes: Lambs page 13, Sheep page 29
Steps page 75, Log fire page 87
Liz Edwards: Bulrushes, pages 40-41
Mary Hallett: Light on the Water, page 57
Joseph Proctor: Break in the Clouds, page 101
Liz Standbrook: Cyprus Beach, page 112

Cover photos by Virginia Duhanes, front cover: Steps leading to Ostrog Monastery, Montenegro

Introduction

I wanted to write a book that wasn't just about people in the Bible who were well known, but also about people who might appear almost as incidental to the story. Yet these people, however small their mention, were of crucial importance in furthering the work of God's kingdom. Again and again it becomes clear how significant and precious each person was, and is, to God.

So, here is the story of an estranged brother (The Reunion, page 4), *a spoilt teenager* (The Dreamer, page 14), *a wealthy princess* (The Unexpected, page 30), *a brilliant commander* (The Foreigner, page 42), *an adulterer* (Betrayal, page 58), *an occupying soldier* (Man of Faith, page 76), *a hunted man* (Called by Name, page 88), *and an elderly couple* (The Faithful, page 102). *Here are stories of the very young and the very old, the privileged and the destitute. Their stepping closer to God transforms not only them, but also the lives of those they touch.*

Just so in our own lives. We too can be led into believing that we are of no importance – that we have no purpose, no role to fulfill. We seem to achieve so little in this busy world. Yet we each hold within us the promise of God. In stepping closer, we see, fleetingly, a glimpse of what God wants us to be.

And God in His infinite wisdom has chosen for us to be born into this time and this place. Only He knows the lives that we might enrich. That really is an exhilarating thought!

Happy reading,

Hilary Faith Jones

Dedication

For Stephen and Emily Rose,
who teach me to step closer.

The Reunion

Prologue

The months had turned into a living nightmare for the expectant mother.
How long she had prayed for a child,
yearned for one,
pleaded, wept to be able to hold that infinitely precious gift in her arms.
And then it had happened.

And she had been so ill.
So desperately sick for weeks on end,
unable to stand,
unable to eat,
unable to work.
The days dragging slowly forward,
the pain wracking her body as the unborn life
twisted and kicked and fought inside her,
tearing her with its ceaseless fighting.
They told her that the birth would be easy after these hellish months
– but they were wrong.
Nothing in the world prepares you for the agony of childbirth.

She watched in a daze as he was born –
a raw, screaming, red, hairy baby.
Angry and vociferous.

The women clapped in delight,
"A boy! A boy!
The heir to his father's house! And strong! And bold!"
How they shouted and laughed.

But then,
as she closed her eyes in dismay,
another child slipped out quietly,
smooth and gentle,
his eyes struggling to find his mother.

And his fingers tightly clutching his brother's heel.

The women pounced in excitement on him.
"Look! Look!" they cried. "He's holding onto his brother!
Using your big brother to pull you into the world.
What a clever little thing you are!"

She reached up,
pushing the ugly, red baby away and took the second one in her arms.
"My son!" she thought.
"This one's mine. Truly mine."
And she held him close and kissed him.

The Reunion

Strange how you wait your whole life for something –
and when it happens it takes you completely by surprise.
There had been no signs,
no difference to the rhythm of the day,
no thought or awareness of the new epoch that lay ahead.

He had strode home that day discussing the abilities of the younger boys with his men.
They were doing well.
Developing into skilled hunters.
Soon they would take over more of the killing, leaving the older men free to remain at home.

He saw the dusty donkeys first – foreign trappings;
then heard the murmur of men's low voices.
His hand went instinctively to his knife.
He quietly stopped his men.

The newcomers had seen him and stood silent,
their heads bowed in respect.
They weren't traders – they were servants.

"Who are you from?"
The oldest of the three stepped slightly forward
and dropped to the ground in a full bow.
"We bring you greetings O Lord –
and pray that God Almighty has greatly blessed you in abundant mercy.
May His goodness fall upon your household
and be witnessed in the prosperity of your sheep…"
He could feel the quick rush of impatience surge up inside him and
had to bite his lip to stop himself interrupting the formalities.
"…may your cattle grow ever stronger…"
The servant still kept his face to the floor as he continued.
And instantly, unnervingly, the hunter was aware of the silence.
Why had all the women disappeared?
Where were the children?
It was too quiet –
a heaviness of silence that lay unbroken.

The servant had finished.
He could feel the hairs stand up on the back of his neck
and fought to control his fingers from tearing his skin –
oh the terrible cursedness of the dry redness that cracked over him,
driving him at times almost insane.

"Who do you bring greetings from?" he snapped.
There was the slightest tremor through the youngest of the servants, a nervous twitch of the foot.
Everything in the hunter was alive, alert, ready for the kill.
"We bring greetings from your brother Jacob."
The ground moved beneath him.
He grasped at the tent rope to steady himself.

The servant hurried on, knowing that he had to fulfil his message.
"Thus says your servant Jacob,
'I have lived with Laban as an alien and stayed until now;
and I have oxen, donkeys, camels, flocks of goats and sheep, male and female slaves; and I have sent to tell my lord, in order that I may find favour in your sight.'"

He couldn't hear the words.
The blood was racing to his head and his heart was pounding.
He felt sick,
breathless,
dizzy.

He waved the servants away.
Jacob. Jacob. Wanting to come home.
Wanting to claim the birthright that should have been his, Esau's.
Except he had so stupidly, so carelessly, thrown it at Jacob's feet.
Now he was coming to take it all.

He ran his fingers through his greying hair,
the violence of the colour faded now with age.
He strode away from the silence, the watching eyes of his people.
Through the fields, pushing the cattle to one side.

O God. O God help me.
Help me know what to do.

twenty years had rolled away
as again in that fateful day –
eeling again the dawning sun begin to warm him,
seeing again the dim, blind eyes of his father turning to him,
his hands clutching at him.
"I am dying Esau," he had whispered. "Bring me food from the fields
that I may bless you."
And he had gone out willingly, spent the day hunting, stalking the finest
prey he could find. Then carefully, his big hands struggling with the
delicacies, he had prepared the meat to please his father.

But his brother Jacob had got there before him.
His cunning, clever, lying brother had tricked their beloved father and
stolen the blessing that was Esau's by right.

He felt the hot tears burn again down his face.
After all these years the memory still heaved inside him.
He saw himself down on his knees, weeping,
begging his father for mercy,
beseeching him for the blessing,
catching his father's gnarled hands
and holding them upon his own head.
"O Father bless me too! I am your first born. Bless me Father.
I beg of you – do not cast me aside."

And his father's voice, choked with tears, trembling with the shock of
the deceit that his younger son had played,
"Away from the fatness of the earth shall your home be,
and away from the dew of heaven on high.
By your sword you shall live and you shall serve your brother…"

The pain of the words had broken Esau.
He had bent his head onto his father's knee and sobbed.
"But…" his father slowly stumbled on,
"when you break loose,
you shall break his yoke from your neck."

Again,
the anger,
the hatred,
the consuming power of revenge flooded the older Esau.
Twenty years on and his brother was finally returning.
Returning from having run from his brother's wrath,
returning to become the master of his brother's land and household.

Esau leaned against a tree, feeling his legs buckle under him.
The strength of those long buried emotions overwhelmed him.
Why, oh why, had their lives gone so wrong?

As brothers, they had been friends.
He was big and rough and crude –
but he had cared for his quieter, gentler brother.
And he had admired the way he understood the flocks,
understanding the subtleties of their movements in a way that was beyond Esau's perception.

But Jacob was also clever.
Clever with words and speech and thought –
and he had twice tricked Esau.
Persuading him into giving his birthright away
(which hadn't been hard because Esau couldn't have cared less about responsibility in those days)
and then stealing their father's blessing.

Aided by their mother.

As he remembered her, Esau's heart contracted within him.
She had consistently pushed him to one side
so that Jacob came to the front;
she had wanted to sit and read the Scriptures with Jacob
but not with him;
she had adored Jacob,
undoubtedly leading him into this final piece of treachery.

What kind of woman was she, that could so schemingly plot to
destroy the bond of brotherhood between them?
He felt again his mother's scorn as she looked at him –
he who was big and ugly and stupid –
and dropped his head into his hands.
"O God help me," he groaned. "I know I'm not clever. I never will be.
But there is good in me. O God believe me.
Do not you too forsake me."
He crumpled on to the ground and wept as he had never done.

The following morning he rose early,
gathering his watchful men to him.
"It is time to go."
Swords were silently slipped into sheaths,
bows oiled, spears sharpened for the last time.
The dust hung in a heavy, ominous cloud over the tents;
the laughter of the children was hushed.
The women knew the cost of what was to come.

They travelled fast and the sun was high in the sky when they saw the first signs of the approaching party. A herd of goats was being driven towards them along the side of the river. The boy herding them ran over to Esau and spoke perfectly, with all the innocence of childhood.
"These goats belong to your servant Jacob.
They are a present to my Lord Esau."
He pointed behind and added, "He is himself coming to you."

Esau stood and stared.
Why would Jacob, returning to enforce the birthright he had stolen,
call Esau 'Lord'?
An appeasement?
Maybe the boy had muddled the words.
He nodded to his men to keep moving but within an hour he was
brought to a halt again.
Another drove swept up to him, this time of sheep.
The message was the same.

The third drove totally stopped Esau in his tracks.
Fine camels.
Twenty, maybe thirty of them, with their young.
His brother was a wealthy man.

Before evening had fallen, two more droves had reached Esau and been sent on to his home. He was a natural hunter and although slightly amused, he was taut with wariness.
The past didn't disappear through gracious gifts.
And despite the cloudless night and heavy stars, suspicion sneaked around his dreams.
Daylight would bring the truth.

Strange.
Just as the news had come upon him unexpectedly,
so now, in the early morning,
they came unexpectedly upon his brother' s camp.

As they topped the hill, filling the horizon with a long line of men, he caused panic in the gathering below.
Women ran back and forth, men stumbled as they strapped their weapons on in haste, children were scooped off the ground.
He waited in silence until they were ready,
trying to pick out his brother in the mêlée.

At last they were grouped in order, ready to receive him.
And then, all alone, out from the crowd came a man.

Esau moved slowly towards him.
Was this his brother?
Where was the lithe, graceful boy that he remembered?
This grey man, dragging himself along with pain etched
across his worn face –
surely this wasn't that handsome youth from twenty years ago?

And then the man looked up.
And in the midst of the man's pain and fear, Esau suddenly caught the glimpse that was his brother.

His breath caught in his great chest.
A terrific surge of overwhelming love filled him.
He stumbled forward, his tears blinding him,
furiously pushing them away.
"JACOB! My brother JACOB!"
His roar seemed to shake the ground.

And then he was in front of him,
his arms reaching out to touch him,
grasp him,
hold onto him.
The man leaned into Esau,
his hands trembling as he clutched at the strong shoulders.

"I want to find favour with you," whispered his brother Jacob.
"For truly, to see the love in your face, is like seeing the face of God."

They held fiercely on to each other, never again to be torn apart.
And the yoke that had bound Esau lay in pieces at their feet,
broken by their reconciliation.

Genesis 33: 1-11
(Genesis 25:24-34; 27:1-45)

As I stand within your presence Lord,
help me to acknowledge the past
so I am aware of all that has shaped me.

May I be given grace Lord,
to grow from my mistakes and failures;

May I be given courage
to let go of the harm that others have done me.

And may I learn the power of forgiveness,
so that I, like Esau,
may greet all with a face that reflects Your Love.

I ask this in the name of Jesus Christ –
who understands all.

The Dreamer

He was the favourite.

His mother absolutely adored him,
showing him off before the others,
blatantly pointing out his natural quickness
against the slowness of his older siblings,
dressing him in clothes of expensive, finer fabric
than those his step-brothers had to share.
They stared, silently, their eyes flitting to their own mothers,
watching them to see if this was good or bad.
His mother laughed delightedly at his turns,
his tantrums,
his snatching away of his brothers' toys.
And then, when the older children complained ferociously,
their voices raised in hot anger,
they were silenced instantly by their father Jacob,
his favour quick to come down on Joseph's side.
The others must learn to share.

Inside,
their natural instinct at fairness at first smarted,
then slowly grew into a seething dislike.
The seeds of jealousy,
of child-anger,
were fostered and stoked,
allowed to grow unhindered and unchecked.

When Joseph's mother died,
he would have felt her death more keenly if it had not been the
source of great attention to him.

He had only to look sorrowful,
to be immediately taken up by his father over the outstretched arms of his brothers;
he had only to fall silent, for his father to brush aside the older children and kneel to play with him.
And as his little brother,
born from the same mother,
grew –
he found yet again that he was adored.
Adulated.
Here at last was the companionship that he wanted but would never receive from his older brothers;
here at last was a brother who would let him play,
would never argue or fight,
would let him totally dominate the game,
being completely submerged by his older brother's forceful personae.
So Joseph's world remained enclosed,
with himself, as always,
the centre of attention.

His older brothers,
born from different mothers,
watched and saw and hated.

To be constantly pushed down,
dismissed, ignored
because of a complacent younger brother
was thoughtless cruelty.

Time and again,
as their father waved them aside,
they began to exchange glances,
whispering quietly to each other,
comforted by the solidarity of their exclusion.

The mothers,
who could have transformed the situation,
did not help.
The two wives – both sisters – had always hated each other.
Rivals for their husband's attention.
Their maids, the other mothers, constantly squabbled.
Maybe then it was no surprise that their children,
the next generation,
seethed with the resentments, real and imaginary,
that were caused by their father's blatant favouritism.

There was an atmosphere of bickering,
of pettiness,
of sides being taken,
of alliances constantly shifting
that permeated the family.
It was a relief really, to have Joseph around
because he did at least manage to bring unity to the household.
In hatred against himself.

So when their father gave the adolescent Joseph the most luxurious robe
– whilst their mothers stitched and patched their own clothing –
the older siblings,
now young men,
had to walk back into their fields to let their anger explode beyond the hearing of their father.
The smouldering fire of hatred had been started at an early age.
Now it was ignited.

And then,
Joseph started dreaming.
He spoke to them one morning with great anticipation,
"Guess what I dreamed of last night? I dreamed we were all binding sheaves in the fields when suddenly..."
He paused and looked to see if they were listening.

"My sheaf leaped up as straight as could be and then, do you know what your sheaves did?"
There was an indifferent silence.
"They all gathered around my sheaf and bowed down low!"
Joseph swept down in a mocking bow, "Just like that!"

Only Reuben bothered to answer, "Sit and eat. It's a long day ahead."
Joseph smiled cockily at them.
They were still cold-shouldering him because he had sneaked unfairly on them the previous week. He had told his father that they had neglected the sheep and fallen asleep when in fact they had merely been resting.

But Joseph was quick and rash
and ready to stir resentment amongst his half-brothers.

So the next time he told of his dreams, he went one step further.

"Can you believe it!" he exclaimed.
"The sun and moon and eleven stars all bowed down to *me*.
Eleven stars!"
He pointedly counted slowly on this fingers. "Eleven! Gosh! The same number as my brothers. Fancy that!"
Gad leaped up in fury.
But before he could speak they were silenced by their father,
who, unfortunately for Joseph, had overheard him.

"What do you mean?" he demanded. "Are you suggesting that I and your mother and your brothers bow low before *you*?"

Joseph blushed fiercely, much to his brothers' pleasure.
Rarely, if ever, did his father speak sternly to him.
"I was just saying about last night..." he stammered.
"Reuben," his father cut across him.
"Tell me your plans for splitting the flock. I think you might need to feed them over at Shechem for a few days first."

Reuben moved to his father's side
and began to discuss the matters of the day.
Joseph sat down quickly,
looking for the first time in his life, rather crushed.

His father listened to Reuben,
nodding his assent every now and then,
but his mind was busy with thoughts of Joseph.

> *"He's such a bright boy!*
> *Dreaming now.*
> *Nature bowing down to him – what does that mean?*
> *Are they messages being sent from God?*
> **My** *Joseph!"*

And he felt his heart swell with pride.

And then somewhere, vaguely,
mixed with the awe in which he held Joseph,
he felt slightly uneasy.
Was it possible that he, Jacob,
who had always been favoured as a child,
had made Joseph precocious?
Conceited? Surely not!
No!
The boy was gifted.
He would go far.
He was special.
Different from the others.

But the occasional 'put down' wouldn't hurt him.

A few days later he called Joseph to him.
"Go and see your brothers over at Shechem and check that all is well with them."

He dropped his hand lightly on the boy's shoulder.
"Then come back home and tell me."
Joseph's heart leaped.
His father wasn't angry with him!
He was restored to his usual place in his affections.

He immediately went and put on his glorious robe.
It made him feel special.
And he liked the way people stared at him.
As he left home and made his way through the Hebron valley,
he lifted his arms
and watched the sun gleam on the threads in the weave.
It really was a splendid present!
No wonder his brothers were jealous.

He reached Shechem and looked for them but there was no sign of the flock or the men. Where on earth were they?
A man with a herd of goats called out,
"Are you alright? Have you lost something?"
Joseph looked round puzzled, "My brothers should have brought our flocks here."
"Are you one of Jacob's boys?"
He nodded.
"They've moved over to Dothan. That way."
The herder pointed out the direction.

Joseph whistled as he walked the distance.
It was a beautiful day.
His father adored him.
Great things lay ahead if his dreams were to be believed.
His dreams!
So vivid and clear!
But strange.
He was obviously destined for greatness!

He passed happily into a daydream which centred around his brothers being made to look foolish.
Some occasion would happen (although he wasn't sure what), which would make him a great hero.
And the whole valley would laud him and exalt him, whilst his jealous, mean, scornful brothers would look up to him, open mouthed, at the feats of bravery he had done.
And despite their behaviour towards him, he would be, in his glory, immensely magnanimous towards them.
And they would be humbled.
It was a pleasant dream and made him smile.

Oh how immature was his understanding, how trite and shallow his interpretation of the divinity of his dreams.

Up in the hills,
Simeon noticed him climbing towards them.
"Look who's coming!" he called out.
The others stood up to see.
"Little brat," muttered Levi. "Flaunting his way along, admiring himself in that stupid coat."
"He's seventeen for pity's sake! He should be out toiling and walking miles in the heat, working night and day like we do.
Not kept at home like a precious little flower."
"I'd love to wipe that smile off his face. Scare the life out of him."

There was a silence,
each thinking of the pleasure it would give to hurt him.
"Especially as we're such a long way from home."
"And its lonely too."

Almost imperceptibly, the atmosphere changed.
Someone, they never could remember who, muttered quietly,
"Wish we could get rid of him."

It was out.
Spoken into the air.
The words that all of them were thinking.
"We can't just kill him. What would we do with his body?"
"Drop it into one of the pits there.
No one would find it for days, weeks."
They stared at each other,
the reality suddenly confronting the fantasy.
"What about his coat?"
"Take it home."
"Covered in blood..."
"Say we found the coat but couldn't find Joseph..."

They hesitated, suddenly scared.
Reuben and Judah appeared over the skyline
and dropped down to them.
"What are you looking at?"
They pointed silently.
"The dreamer!" scoffed Judah.
"We're going to kill him!" Zebulun burst out, his voice, body, shaking with pent-up emotion.
Reuben stared, startled. "You can't kill him, Zebulun
– much as you might like to."
He spoke lightly and then realised with a sinking heart
that they were being serious.
"We've had enough of his puffed-up conceit."
The men were mutinous,
the idea of death now forming quickly, urgently, within them.
An end in sight to the lifelong problem.
The thought, growing into solid possibility, no longer shocked them.
This was real. They didn't want Reuben to hold them back.

Reuben looked around at their hardening faces.
"No," he said firmly. "No! We cannot take his life."
He saw them fingering their knives. "Or take his blood."
He thought quickly.

If Joseph was unharmed,
he could rescue him later and get him back home.
A few hours in misery wouldn't damage him.
"Strip him and leave him in the pit. But do not hurt him."

They glanced rebelliously at each other,
torn between the red mist of violence,
the smell of blood,
the heady chance of revenge –
and the relief of being able to walk away from it, of behaving normally.

Joseph was now within earshot,
clambering up the rocky stones, pushing his way past a knot of sheep.
"Hello!" he called. "I've brought you food!"
He held it out to Asher
before noticing that they were all staring intently at him.

It was their silence that got him.
"What?" he looked at them. "What's the matter with you?
Never seen food before?"
He'd meant it to be funny but it sounded mocking, jeering,
as if they were stupid.

Looking back,
it all happened in slow motion.
The bag of food swinging back and forth in his outstretched arm;
the men watching, waiting;
the sound of the sheep eating the grass.
The emptiness, the isolation of the spot.

And then,
like a pack of wolves,
they started to silently edge closer.
He could feel the heat from their bodies,
their breath in his face –
hands, feet, clutching at hair,
struggling, crying, screaming, fighting.
The robe was gone.
Bare skin.
Ashamed.
Vulnerable.
Frightened.
Hands clawing at him, punching him, bruising him.
Lifting him as he twisted and turned and writhed in their grip.
A tremendous noise, shouting, crying.
Falling.
Pain as he hit the ground.

"This isn't funny!" he screamed up at them from the darkness of the pit. "Get me out of here!"

It was so humiliating.
The burning fury of anger, impotence, frustration.
He screamed furiously at them like a little child.
"How dare you!
When father knows he'll kill you.
He'll KILL you!"
He screamed until he was hoarse.
They leant over the edge, mocking, pointing, laughing.
"Leave him!" said Reuben and drew them away. "Let him be."

They were exuberant.
High on the excitement of the fight,
shouting to each other,
leaping on each other,
heady with the success of ten against one.

They took his robe and the bag of food,
throwing the bread loaves to each other,
laughing too loudly.
Exhilarated.

Uneasy,
Reuben left with Issachar and Dan to take care of the flocks grazing over the hill.
The others slowly began to relax, joking with each other,
waiting in anticipation
for the next insult that came screeching up from the pit,
falling around with laughter as they listened.

They hadn't had such a day in years!
Revenge felt wonderfully good.

They watched the caravan of camels slowly, heavily, picking its way across the hillside.
"Coming from Gilead, I guess." said Naphtali.
"What have they got?" Asher couldn't be bothered to sit up and look.
"Gum, resin – maybe balm."
"I wonder how far away Egypt really is." Gad had always wanted to travel and watched the train enviously.
"A long way!" they said in unison and then laughed together.

"A long way," murmured Judah.
He stared at the line, patiently weaving its way.
"I wonder how much they'd pay for a slave?"
Asher looked at him. "What d'you want a slave for?"
"A young, strong, beautiful-looking boy."
The others sat up and stared at him.
"You mean…?"
Judah nodded. "D'you think we could do it?"
"We'd be getting rid of him for ever," said Gad slowly, "without hurting a hair of his head."

They looked at Judah,
catching their breath as the idea took hold.
"And Reuben is right you know – he is our brother. Our own flesh. We can't kill him..."
"And Reuben won't be back until dusk..."
Judah strode down the hill, waving to the caravan to stop.
"Wait for my signal before you get him out."
There was much noise and shouting and grunting as the camels came to a halt,
sinking to their knees before lowering their hind legs.
They bared their teeth and spat loudly at the keepers.
The smell was overwhelming.

"We have a slave to sell."
The negotiations opened. "Strong, young, healthy."
The Ishmaelite pondered. "I want to see him."
Judah waved to his brothers.

They lowered the rope down and suddenly Joseph felt like crying.
For the last few minutes he had been quiet
for his throat was raw with screaming.
And into that quietness had come such a fear.
Supposing they left him there?

All alone.
In that desolate spot.
No one would ever find him.
He would surely die, his body growing colder and colder.
The terror crept over him.

How he wished now to be with his brothers.
Never again would he lord it over them,
never again would he outsmart them in conversation
or draw his father's attention to himself.
Never again would he drift uselessly around trying to annoy them.
If only they would be nice to him.

He curled up in a tight ball and rocked back and forth.
And then he heard them and the rope came snaking down.
The relief was almost unbearable!

They had just been teasing him!
Bullying him, punishing him.

As he came up to the top of the pit and felt freedom again,
the old anger came flowing back.
    How dare they!
    They would pay for this.
    He would tell Father and he would *never* forgive them.
His mind began to think furiously of ways to punish them.

But the moment he was out,
his brothers were busy, pushing his hands behind him, tying him tight.
He struggled and fought but to no avail.
He was pushed face down in the earth whilst they bound him,
then pulled him roughly to his feet.
"He's filthy dirty. Hang on a minute."
Gad threw water in his face.
Joseph gasped at the shock,
the water running down from his hair into his eyes.
"Get a cloth – clean him up a bit!"

What on earth was going on?

They led him down the slope.
For a moment he didn't understand and then he saw Judah standing
with the Ishmaelite trader.
He knew immediately and crying out he turned to run.
They leaped at him as he bucked and screamed, "NO! Judah! NO!"

His brothers were sweating, holding him fiercely by his arms and legs.
The trader came over, roughly taking hold of Joseph's jaw.
He tried to yank his face away.

His shoulders and muscles were squeezed by the man;
his hands and feet inspected.
He nodded to Judah. "We'll take him."

"NO!"
Every muscle, every sinew, every part of him screamed in terror.
"For God's sake Judah! Save me!"

But the price had been settled.
Twenty pieces of silver.

"Asher! Gad! Simeon! Please!
I'll do anything. I swear. Please! Help me!
Don't leave me with this man . . . ."

But his cries went unheeded.
His brothers didn't even look at him, they were too busy fastening him to a camel, their eyes on the money.

There was a cracking of whips and the camels,
grumbling and vicious,
were pulled to their feet.

They started moving.

He dug his feet into the ground.

"Judah – I beg you. Help me!"
Judah came over and spoke very quietly.
"What will become of your dreams now,
you arrogant, big-headed little boy?
We're glad to be rid of you.
You know nothing about being part of a family."

The camel moved away, dragging Joseph with him.
"I'm sorry! I'm sorry!" he called frantically.
"I'm sorry. I'll change – I swear!"

His brothers turned and walked away.
They did not watch the long line of camels as it inexorably continued its journey to a distant land.
They did not listen to the cries of their brother which could be heard for a long time,
until the hills enclosed him and he was finally gone,
taken from their sight and from their lives.

As they counted the money,
the silver catching the light on that once again isolated hillside,
what could they know of the future;
of the hardships that lay in front of them
or the strangeness of the journeys that lay before Joseph?
What could they possibly understand of the power of good?

For they did not know until years later
when they had been changed by sorrows,
that if a person opens up to God,
then from awful human tragedies
God can bring good.

Just so with Joseph
whose heart was broken.
Good would come through the gifts of his growing in grace.

The dreamer had gone.
But his dream telling had yet to begin.

Genesis 37

O God
In the loneliness of our pain,
when we cannot see the dawn of any future,
when grief and desolation break us
and life is too unbearable to live –
hold us fast God,
for only you can bring good out of terrible suffering.

Bring us, O God,
from these ashes of despair
to a profounder understanding of the resurrection hope.

The Unexpected

The maid gently shook her shoulder until she stirred,
reluctantly opening her eyes.
It was time.
She was still young enough to want to clutch at
the warmth of slumber
yet old enough to be profoundly moved by the still-dark,
the coldness in the air,
the expectancy of waiting in the darkened temple for the first signs of
the sun-god.

It was always a miracle to her.
The rising of Re,
the assurance that good would win over evil,
that life would always rise from death.
For the Princess Merris,
the stories of Osiris, Iris, Re – all the gods – became one in that
extraordinary moment when the light of the rising sun
shot across the darkened sky,
touching the altar table with liquid gold;
suffusing the windows,
waking the deep shadows,
warming the air.
The miracle of life.
The hope of a new day.

The morning wonder over,
she idled her way back to the palace,
surrounded by the noise and clutter and bustle
of the day unfolding.

Already Re seemed to be hanging heavily,
his light playing on the water,
the heat beginning to gather on the ground.

Today, she decided, she would bathe.

As she passed through the cool corridors,
the cat came out of the shadows and wove himself
into her legs.
She held her breath.
He leaned against her, waiting for attention,
opening his mouth wide in a perfect yawn.
The tiny white razor sharp teeth
against the gleaming black of his fur.
His eyes gazed at her,
amber pools, unblinking,
keeping their mystery untold.
Bored,
he wandered into a patch of sunlight and
unceremoniously began to wash himself.

She dropped him a low bow
thanking him for his graciousness towards her.
It was a good omen.
It meant that Bastet,
the cat-headed goddess,
was watching over her.
As she left,
she glanced back to see if he was following.
The cat had stretched himself out,
totally oblivious to the world,
enjoying the warm sunlight
that fell in a golden streak across the dim corridor.
As the royal servants and officials hurried to their work,
they had to juxtapose bowing to him
whilst squeezing against the wall to pass,
for it was unthinkable to intrude upon his space.
She felt an irresistible giggle as she watched them.
Bastet clearly had a sense of humour.

Her serving girls chatted gaily with her as they made their way to the river.
They were glad of the freedom to get away from the palace – away from the orders of the older women who made them work endlessly for them.
Bathing allowed the chance of lazing,
of gossiping with each other,
of taking a long time to comb and dress the Princess's hair,
of daydreaming and doing very little.

They hesitated at the market place,
waiting for instructions.
She indicated the long way round.
Never again would she take the direct route for that passed near to the slaves' dwellings.
Never again did she wish to witness the horror that had burst across her day a few months earlier.
It flashed now,
unbidden,
upon her inner mind.

The speed of the soldiers,
their snatching of the tiny ragdoll of a baby,
the terror of the mother's screaming –
the desperation,
the frenzy,
the terrible sound of a womans' mind being tipped into insanity.
The swirling dust,
the noise,
the pounding hooves.

Then it was over.
Before any of them had had time to move, the soldiers had gone.
And slowly the dust settled upon a young mother
screaming over the body of her newborn child.

It had taken a long time to get that image out of her mind.
Of course she knew the slaves were too populous;
of course she understood that measures had to be taken to limit their numbers;
of course they couldn't have too many males.
Yet to hear the soldiers being given their orders was one thing;
to actually see it,
hear it,
breathe it,
was terrifying.

Again and again,
the scene had come into her thinking, haunting her;
again and again,
she had wondered if there was not a better way to control the male population of slaves;
again and again,
she caught herself looking at slaves who were with child
and was amazed at their naivety, their belief that they carried a girl.
And again and again,
she had secretly wondered –
what would she do if she was a slave?
What would she do to save her own child?

Awful questions that slipped into her mind –
disturbing her,
niggling at her when she should be enjoying herself,
casting an unspoken pall over her pleasures.
Ruthlessly driving her to think the unthinkable –
the questioning of the very fundamentals that ruled, governed her life.

But today she would not think of those things.
Today it was hot.
And she would slip into those cool waters and feel the blessings of Re cover her.

And the girls would smooth creams and perfume into her skin
and comb her hair with oils
and twirl it and braid it and thread it with tiny beads,
until she truly shone as only a Princess could.
She chose a site further away from the city.
Here the bulrushes grew thickly along one section of the river and
long-legged herons flapped away effortlessly from the chattering girls.
They set up her screens away from the reeds –
and with much giggling and laughing
helped her to change her robes,
piling with much glee
the bathing sheets upon the maid who would accompany her.
She was the only one who didn't look enamoured at the expedition –
for the Princess loved to linger in the water
whilst her poor maid,
swimming with her,
struggled to hold the sodden sheets in a vain attempt
to preserve the Princess' purity from prying eyes.
The maid looked at the cold water and sighed.

It wasn't long before the Princess had swum to the deepest part of
the river.
And it was then, looking back to the bank,
that she noticed a basket of some sort, tightly lodged within the reeds.
She stared at it a moment,
thinking that if she swam a few strokes further to the side,
it would disseminate and turn out to be a broken oar
or a bird's nest or a pile of debris.
But it didn't.
It still looked like a basket.

She pointed to it.
"There's a basket there. Go and bring it."
The maid hesitated, somewhat laden with the modesty sheet.
"Give it to me."
Merris impatiently took hold of the sheet and pushed at the girl.

"You can stand up over there. Go and get it."
She still hesitated.
"There are 'things' in those reeds," the maid said.
"There'll be 'things' in your bed tonight if you don't hurry up,"
the Princess retorted furiously. "Bring it to me *now*."
She started back to the waiting girls,
dragging the sheet behind her in the water.
She hadn't realised how heavy it was –
no wonder her maid looked so mutinous.

Disappointed that the Princess had finished so soon,
the girls stirred and got ready to wrap her in fresh robes.
She pushed them away.
"I want to see."
The maid was slowly pulling behind her some sort of woven basket –
it looked almost like a miniature boat.
It was obviously heavy as it kept bumping into her as she waded
towards them along the edge of the bank.
She pushed the basket towards them and clambered out.
"What is it?"
"What's inside?"
"I bet it's gold!"
"Maybe it's from the robbery at one of the temples last week ...."
The girls clustered around the Princess, pressing to see.
She bent to look and started back in shock.
Under the cover was a baby, fast asleep,
its chest rising softly up and down.
The girls went into a twitter of excitement.

"It's one of them slave babies!"
"Look at its face – it's so sweet!"
"Yeah – but it's a Hebrew. You can tell."
"But it's still sweet – poor thing."
"Fancy leaving it in a basket!"
"Them slaves are proper cruel you know!"
"Is it a boy ma'am? I bet it is!"

She looked carefully.

It was a boy.
He opened his eyes and stared at her and began to cry.
A tiny wail that filled her with a sudden rush of compassion.
Without thinking,
she picked him up and drew him close to her,
rocking him gently like she'd seen the feeding women do.
"What are you going to do ma'am?"
"He's probably been left here to die, hasn't he?"
She looked at the basket.
Someone had made it with care. There were no leaks.
And the blanket he was wrapped in was fresh and clean,
with tiny patterns embroidered on it.
The little world in which he lay had been created by love.
This baby had been hidden.

Again she saw that desperate image –
the mother screaming silently as she held her broken baby.
The Princess pressed him closer.

A thousand thoughts rushed through her,
tumbling her mind.
What should she do?

Take him home and look after him herself?
Impossible!
She didn't know what to do with a baby.
Couldn't possibly feed it or care for it.

Take him home and give him to one of the feeding mothers?
Impossible!
No Egyptian would feed a slave baby or care for him.
He would come to an unexplained end.

Put him back and hide him again?
Impossible!
The girls could not be kept quiet about this.
They would talk and soon everyone would know.
The child would be found and killed.

Put him back and wait for the mother?
Impossible!
The girls would still talk.
The soldiers would soon root out the mother.
Both might be destroyed.

There was so much noise going on –
so much exclaiming and declaring and theorising –
that no one noticed the little slave girl standing awkwardly at the edge of the bulrushes.
Where she had come from, no one knew.
But she was watching them intently.
And she had heard their talk.

"Ma'am, there's a slave girl watching," whispered one of the girls.
The Princess stood up, still holding the baby
and slowly walked over to the little girl.
She smiled at her and knelt down beside her.
Instinctively the girl's hand touched the baby then quickly withdrew.
"What's your name?" the Princess asked.
The child's eyes flew to the Princess',
huge eyes full of fear.
"Miriam." She whispered.
"We've found a baby." The Princess spoke softly.
"What are we going to do?"
Again the eyes flew to her face –
searching, questioning,
flickering between despair and hope.

"Well." The little girl hesitated.
"You need someone to nurse babies you know."
The Princess nodded.
"But I don't know anyone."
"I do!" The words were out before the Princess had finished speaking.
"My Mum's really good with babies. Would you like her to look after this one?"

The princess smiled.
"Do you think your mother would do that for me?"
"Oh yes!" The child nodded vigorously.
"Then tell her to come to the Palace – and ask for Princess Merris.
I shall be waiting for her."
She went back to the gossiping girls.
"Come! We're going back."
They rushed around, trying to pack up everything in a hurry,
sorry to have missed an indolent morning
but with *such* a tale to tell!

Still the little girl lingered, unsure of what to do.
"Quickly Miriam! Fetch your mother!" ordered the Princess.
And with that the child was gone, bare feet flying over the ground,
brown arms and legs and hair.

"What are you going to do ma'am?"
"You're never going to keep it?"
"What's the Pharaoh going to say?"
She silenced their impertinent talk with an imperial look.
Their eyes dropped and they fell quiet,
obediently following her,
nudging each other as soon as her back was turned.

With great pride,
she carried the baby.
It was all quite clear now.

This was why she had been so moved by Re this morning;
this was why Bastet's cat had singled her out,
this was why she had swum in a different area to normal –
all the signs were explained now.
She felt she'd been guided to the place to find the baby.
And now he was hers.
Just as her father had the right to choose life or death,
so she too would exercise that royal power.
And she chose life.

"What are you going to call him ma'am?"
One of the girls, emboldened by the others, ventured to ask.
Princess Merris stopped and thought.
And then smiled.
"Moses."
"Moses?" whispered one of the girls. "Why is she calling him 'born'?"
"Because," replied the Princess, "now he *is* born.
Pulled from the bulrushes – and given life."

She looked back as she reached the Palace gates.
Somewhere,
in that heaving, dusty city,
a mother was running to her,
holding the hand of a little girl,
with hope in her heart.
"Maybe that's what you bring," she mused,
gazing down into the baby's face.
"Maybe, Moses, you bring hope."
And she smiled as the rays of the sun-god
slanted across his face.

Exodus 2:1-10

For those who use their wealth and power to bring good,
I raise my thanks to you O God.

For those who are different to me,
yet seek truth and light,
I raise my thanks to you O God.

For those who take risks and seize the opportunity,
I raise my thanks to you O God.

For those who think and question
and are prepared to defy the status quo,
I raise my thanks to you O God.

May I
be ready to respond to your call,
even if I might never know the reason why.

Lord God,
who moves in deep and mysterious ways,
hear my prayer.

The Foreigner

He entered the courtyard at a gallop,
something he had always loved doing.
He loved the furious speed with which he rode,
loved the way people moved aside and stared after him,
whispering his name;
loved to shout, to boom out his commands in a voice that was deep and thunderous;
loved thinking, planning, devising strategies as he watched his men train,
his mind busy with probabilities and possibilities;
loved the smell of leather, the warmth of his horse, the biting cold of campaign trails and the hazy folds of the hills at home;
loved the sheer drama, the recklessness, the excitement of living;
loved captivating people by his sheer charisma – servants, slaves, friends, children – it didn't matter.

Fluent and articulate, he was a natural leader.
The men he commanded would die for him;
he was held in the highest esteem of the king – one of the most trusted and admired commanders ever known.
And he was adored at home.
He was an exceptional man –
big in stature,
big in respect.

Life should have been glorious.

He swept into his house, flinging his cloak off,
striding through the rooms calling his children.
They fell upon him,
shrieking with excitement as he threw them in the air,
sweeping them low in dizzying circles.
His wife appeared in the doorway and watched smiling.

"Enough, children," she said. "Go and find your lunch, it's ready for you."
They peeled themselves away from their father,
dodging out of the reach of his fingers.
"Go and eat now, you mischievous scoundrels," he roared
as they ran off.

He lay back on the couch.
"When did they grow so big?" he sighed.
His wife made no answer; instead she was looking at his feet.
She knelt on the floor and started to undo his sandals.
"The King was pleased with you?"
"Of course. I'm his favourite commander."
She began rubbing his toes, calling out "Sarah!"
A young slave girl appeared.
"Bring me a bowl of warm water and the lavender from my room."
The girl nodded and disappeared.
"How is little Sarah getting on?" he asked.
His wife smiled.
"Much better. She no longer cries herself to sleep.
She's such a sweet girl. I'm glad you brought her to me."
He put his hand on her hair and stroked it.
"Thank heavens we're on the winning side.
At least here, she'll get a good home."
The slave girl returned and quietly knelt by her mistress, handing her the things that were needed.
"Can you feel this?" His wife pinched his toe, gradually moving up his foot looking for a reaction.
There was none.
"What about this?" she moved to another toe. "Or this?"
He watched her face and tried to smile. "It's getting worse, isn't it?"
She felt choked up inside with the rising fear.
"There must be someone, somewhere." she whispered.
"We've got the money, Naaman. We'll sell everything – the house, the horses, the land – everything! If we can only get you well."
She looked up at him desperately.
Her husband avoided her eyes.

For in their hearts
they both knew that the future held no hope.

Later,
as the household settled for bed,
the slave girl slipped into the wife's room.
She started on her mistress' hair,
brushing it rhythmically with long sweeps.
The mistress watched her in the mirror and after a moment put her hand on the girl's arm,
"Is there something wrong, Sarah? Tell me – don't bottle it all up."
"Oh Ma'am!"
The slave girl fiddled the brush awkwardly between her fingers.
"It's the master's feet."
Her mistress smiled sadly and held the girl's hand.
"I know. It's awful to see. We all bear his pain too."
The girl shook her head. "No, it's not that."
"Oh!" The mistress looked in surprise at her and embarrassed,
the girl rushed quickly on.
"It's just that it looks the same as my neighbour's fingers. You know, back home. She couldn't feel anything either and kept hurting herself all the time. One day she poured boiling water all over her hand and didn't even know she'd done it – and all the skin blistered up and an infection got in…"
"Yes, thank you Sarah!" Her mistress cut her off sharply, a muscle twitching in her face.
"But Ma'am, she got better!"
The mistress spun around to face her.
"What did you say?"
"She got better! She went to see this man …"
The mistress grabbed her and held her tightly –
"What man? What man Sarah? What was his name?"
The girl stopped and thought .
"I don't know his name. He lived in the hills."
The mistress gazed at the girl hardly daring to breathe.
The sudden shot of hope across her was almost painful.

"Oh Sarah, supposing he could make Naaman better!
I'll give anything, anything to have him healed."
She whirled to the doorway,
"Naaman! Naaman! Come quickly!"

They set the slave girl down on the couch and made her tell them exactly what she knew. She tried to remember as much as she could but it remained vague and disjointed.

"I'll need permission from the King to go into Israel. They might not take kindly to me – the truce is still fragile."
His wife clutched him. "But you will go won't you? Please Naaman! Go and find this man and do whatever he asks. I beg you!"
He was silent, drawing away from the enormity of what lay before him.
It meant asking the King, to ask a favour, of a conquered people and that involved all kinds of political ramifications;
it meant waiting upon the good will of a defeated King,
of begging men he might well have fought against in battle, to help him;
it involved travelling through an alien land,
of a people whose blood he had shed.
It meant weeks away from home, in the hottest time of the year;
it meant asking a foreigner,
from another religion, to heal him.

And all this,
on the slight evidence
of a girl who was a slave.
It just wasn't feasible.
But then, the future held a slow, sickening, isolated, living death.

"I'll ask the King in the morning," he said.

Many weeks later, he stood in the archway of a foreign palace
looking out over a different landscape.
Outside his servants were uneasy,
watching over the heavy bags that contained an immense fortune –
the luxurious clothing of the finest silks and the money.
Thousands and thousands of gold shekels.
No wonder his servants were worried,
fingering their weapons nervously as the foreign palace guards silently watched them.
He was putting all their lives in jeopardy.

A palace official appeared and bowed to him,
respectful yet dignified.
The doors were opened and he was admitted into the King of Israel's ante-chamber.
He strode up to the King with his usual speed, holding out the precious letter.
It only occurred to him later that what was decisive action to him,
might appear as arrogance to others.

The King eyed him coldly –
this hardened warrior striding arrogantly around his palace –
broke open the seal and read the brief note.

When this letter reaches you,
know that I, King of Aram,
have sent to you my servant Naaman,
that you may cure him of his leprosy.

The King of Israel looked up startled at Naaman.
He then re-read the letter.
He politely bowed.
"Accommodation will be found for you and your servants while we deal with this request."
Naaman bowed in return and thanked him formally.
There was nothing more he could do.
He had to wait upon this King's instruction.

As soon as Naaman had left the room the King exploded.
"Have you seen this?" He waved the letter furiously.
"What tricks are the Arameans playing at now? Read it, just read it!"
His anger was smouldering around him, threatening to ignite the air.
"It's quite obvious – he's trying to pick a quarrel with me so he can send in his armies. And what's more – that man…"
He stabbed the air in the direction that Naaman had taken.
"That man is no other than Naaman, the great and favoured commander."
He rounded on his advisor who was frowning over the letter.
"He's sent him to me so I can cure him of his leprosy.
Who does he think I am? God, all of a sudden?
Giving life to others?"
He picked up his cloak and tempestuously tore it,
flinging it down the hall.
Then he flung his sword after it.
"How can I cure leprosy? I am *not* God!"

His advisor watched him whilst thinking rapidly.
"Do nothing my lord. Nothing for the moment.
It is best to wait and see what happens."
The King flung himself into his chair and fumed.
"They're out to make trouble. And we have not the strength or resources – or will – in us for a long fight."
"I don't know," the advisor replied thoughtfully.
"That man had an honest face. It might be quite genuine."
"Well that's no help to me at all," the King snapped back exasperated.
"I'm still not God you know."
The advisor suppressed a smile.
"We'll send out messengers and see what we can do."
And then catching the King's eye, he added, "Discreetly of course."

Within a few days a response came to the Palace.
"I have a message from a man who calls himself a prophet of God," the King's advisor murmured.
"What man?" The King demanded.
"He goes by the name of Elisha."

"Elisha!" breathed the King and sat silent.
Elisha, the rudest, most disrespectful, insulting, demeaning, bald-headed little man in his entire kingdom.
His name still rankled in the King's memory after their last encounter.
Yes!
Elisha could deal with this wealthy, handsome, leperous foreigner.
And if it went wrong, there would only be Elisha to blame.

The King stroked his beard and a gleam came into his face.
If Elisha succeeded, it reflected well on the King.
If he failed,
at least the King would have the satisfaction of dealing with this so-called prophet.
Either way, the King won.
"Tell the commander that the King sends him to the man named Elisha."
And he smiled at his most charming.

Naaman breathed a sigh of relief.
At last they were moving, travelling one step nearer to the end purpose of their journey.
To a man of immediate action, these last few days of waiting had been immensely irksome.
Movement meant purpose.
He whistled as he supervised the loading of the chariots and checked his horse's hooves.
They were finally reaching the end of all these weeks.
And then the knot tightened in his stomach in sick worry.

The sun glittered upon their garments and trappings
as they approached the prophet's home,
one of the few houses scattered across the hillside.
The cavalcade stopped outside and Naaman nodded to his servant to enter and announce his arrival.
Not that the prophet could be in any doubt with the amount of noise they had made and the grey cloud of dust that hung over them.

As he waited, Naaman surveyed the house. Built in the style of the country, it lacked the finesse that came with wealth.
It was basic, poor, shabbily built.
The dirty matting hanging over the flat roof needed replacing.
"Prophets are clearly not prized in this country," he thought to himself.
What sort of man would he be?
Naaman was a good judge of character – with men that was.
Women were so much more complicated.
But he would know when he looked into the prophet's face what calibre of manhood he was to deal with.
Whether this prophet spoke with truth or falseness.

His servant came out of the dark house.
"The prophet says that you are to wash in the Jordan seven times – then your flesh will be restored and you will be made clean."

Naaman stared at him, momentarily speechless.
"But when is he going to come and examine me?"
"He didn't seem to think it necessary, my lord."

Naaman drew back as the insult hit.
This poverty stricken man thought himself above speaking to one of the greatest commanders of the age?
Did he not know that he had travelled for many weeks to reach this place?
That he had had to go through the humiliating process of servants, courtiers, kings –
all talking about him,
standing away from him?
Didn't he know that all the hopes of Naaman's life were caught into that miserable little house?

The fear inside him gave way to anger.
He ordered his servant back into the chariot and jabbed at his horse's mouth to pull her around. Her ears flickered in surprise at such rough handling and she bucked.

He cracked the whip over her,
sending her galloping back to the dirt road.
The cavalcade behind were much slower to move.
They had all begun to relax, sensing the end of the journey.
His sudden departure startled them;
there was much shouting and turning of horses
and stamping of hooves.

He galloped unchecked for a mile then brought her to a stop under the shade of a tree.
She was sweating,
froth flicked over her nose and neck, her sides heaving.
It was far too hot to drive an animal at that speed.
Being an experienced soldier he got out of his chariot and guiltily went to calm her down.
But he was burning with anger.

His servant climbed out beside him. They stood silent in the hot shade.
"How dare he?" Naaman spoke through clenched teeth.
"How dare he speak to me like that?"
He could feel himself trembling inside, like a child.
"As if we don't have beautiful waters in our own land – a thousand times cleaner than their muddy Jordan."
The servant,
who had been with him since the commander had been an impulsive youth,
waited patiently.
"I need him to see me,
to say the right words over me.
I need to feel the heat of his healing as he moves his hands over my feet.
He has got to summon his god.
That's what healing's all about."

The servant said nothing.
He understood that the insult was,
quite simply,
the last straw in the many weeks of encroaching darkness;
that a man, however strong,
can only be pushed so far before he breaks;
that his lord was struggling
with the overwhelming blindness and hopelessness of an unstoppable disease that would kill him.
"You know, my lord," he said gently. "If he had told you to do something very difficult, you would have done it immediately."

Naaman glanced at his old servant but said nothing.
"So why not do this thing? It's easy to do. Bathe – seven times.
And if it doesn't work, we'll go home. But at least you have done what we came all this way to do."

Naaman pulled his mare's head towards him, slowly rubbing her nose.
She snorted and butted his chest, soothed by his hands.
"How many campaigns have we travelled together?" he asked.
The servant thought for a moment. "Too many to count, my lord."
"And how many times have we saved each other?"
The servant laughed. "Too many to count, my lord."
Naaman looked steadily at him until the noise of their companions distracted him.

The rest of the party,
in some disarray, came into sight.
The servant watched them.
"What shall I tell them, my lord?"
Naaman looked the other way, smarting with the anger.
The servant's gaze looked up into the intense blueness of the sky.
"It's such a hot day, my lord. A swim might just be what's needed."
A reluctant smile edged across Naaman.
The servant noticed and walked across to the waiting group.
"Turn around, we're heading for the river."

The first few times he bathed
he made a terrific noise;
shouting, splashing, spraying water on to the servants who bathed with him, dunking them.
It was almost like a holy day,
when all the families went to the river for enjoyment.
But slowly, one by one,
they tired and clambered out onto the bank,
fell asleep or dozed, stretched out in the shade.

After his fourth swim he was on his own.
And from then onwards he found each bathe increasingly hard.
For a man of action,
he found it suddenly very quiet;
almost lonely.
He liked to be surrounded by noise and people
and loudness and laughter.
Like the reassurance of the zest of life.

But now it seemed it was just him.
And the blue sky stretched unbroken above him and the hot sun blazed down.
And the silence grew.

He floated on his back,
eyes closed,
a strange feeling gradually slipping over him.
His thoughts, which usually raced around,
were fading from him;
He became acutely aware
of the lapping of the water,
the faintest whisper of a breeze,
the unfamiliar rushing sound of his own blood pumping through his body.
Everything slowing down.
Stillness beginning to fill him, hold him.

It was as if he was suspended –
a part of life
and yet, he was away from it, at a distance.
In some other place.
He felt beautifully sleepy,
yet increasingly alert,
more in tune and at one with everything happening around him
than he had ever been.

He became,
at last,
completely still.
Quiet.
Motionless.
And it was then that he felt it.
Something approaching that made his heart beat faster;
he daren't move.
Held his breath,
terrifyingly aware that he was coming into the presence of something
far beyond his experience.

And suddenly,
a great, wonderful, fulfilling, all-encompassing sense of peace swept
through him.
He wanted to cry
but couldn't move.
His chest ached with unshed tears.
He wanted to stay there for ever,
held in this fleeting place of beauty.
But the sounds of his companions,
of a horse snorting,
of a wheel being hammered,
were becoming louder.
He was coming back to them.
And the inbetween place was disappearing,
slipping through the fingers of his mind.

It was time. Time to return.
He opened his eyes and began to swim slowly back.
He was changed.
Something indescribable had happened,
for he had been in the presence of God.
And now he was different.

He climbed out and walked over to his old servant.
He felt strange. Quiet inside.
Tremulous.
He wanted to tell someone. Share it.

His foot hit a sharp stone and he winced, glancing down.
The nail had torn and there was blood oozing out.
He looked back up and saw his servant staring at him, eyes wide.
Naaman frowned, puzzled.
And then it hit him.

He looked down again at his foot.
He had felt it!
He had felt the stone hit his toes,
felt the uncomfortable stab as it jagged his skin.
He stared.
Then moved his foot up and down,
pressing the toes back and forth into the ground.
"O God!" he whispered.
He could feel it!
Could feel every joint, every little bone, every piece of dirt that clung to his wet feet.
He could feel, where before there had been deadness.
He looked back at his faithful servant.
The older man had tears running down his cheeks.

Naaman fell to his knees
with a great roar of delight,
shattering the still day.

Flung his arms wide to the sky –
"Thank you, thank you O great God of all!
I live! I live! Thank you!"

And slowly, led by the old servant,
his fellow travellers fell to their knees and knelt beside him.

They went back of course.
Back to the shabby little house and the rude man of God.
He was waiting for them.
Leaning against his doorway, watching them,
listening to their high spirits and shouts and laughter.

Naaman leaped from his chariot,
and stood breathless, towering over the man of God.
His face told Elisha everything.
"Now I know.
There is no God in all the earth except your God.
The God of Israel."
He hesitated because he was trying to learn about God and
everything was still so new.
"Please accept a present from me, your servant."
Elisha shook his head, his eyebrows slightly raised.
"Please!" Naaman pressed. "I have so much! Take what you like –
clothes, money…"
Elisha stared steadily at him.
"As the Lord lives, whom I serve, I will accept nothing!"
Something inside, told Naaman not to argue.
"May I beg one more favour from you?
Will you allow me to take some soil from your land home with me?
I worship your God from now on.
The gods I used to worship are all gone.
I believe – in your God.
The one and only God of all."

For a moment Elisha and Naaman looked at each other.
Bound by the love of God.
Then Naaman turned to go.
"Oh!" he turned back,
another problem raising itself suddenly in his mind.
He loved his King.
His King who had loved him and supported him and risked all kinds of political ramifications for him. He could not turn from a man who was both his King and his friend.

"I have a problem!" He whispered.
"When my King goes into the house of his god Rimmon to worship,
he leans on me. I am his trusted servant.
And, like the King, I have always bowed to Rimmon too.
The next time I enter Rimmon's house and bow to him,
will your God grant me pardon?"

Elisha thought about God.
So much bigger, beyond all of this.
Naaman was only just beginning his journey of faith.
He had much to learn.
"Go my friend," he said,
his face suffused with the light of God.
Strange.
Just for a moment,
he looked quite beautiful.

He laid his hand upon the great commander,
who had travelled long to find God.
"Go in peace."

So Naaman went home.
Back to his country.
To live and work for God's praise and glory.

And God was with him.

2 Kings 5:1–19

When I hear a child speak,
teach me to listen carefully Lord –
for the little ones walk so closely,
so easily, holding your hand.

When I hear the old speak,
teach me to put my will aside –
for the elderly have so much wisdom that comes from long journeys and long talks with you.

When I hear my loved ones speak,
teach me not to rush –
but to think slowly over their words,
for they speak out of your love God.

When I hear a foreigner speak,
teach me to look behind the appearance –
and remember that you use the most unexpected people to spread your truth.

And when I am desolate,
facing a bleak future,
teach me to lift my eyes to the cross.
And know that Christ walks with me,
every step of the way.

Betrayal

The light was just beginning to ease across the sky,
when she crept, a silent shadow, out of the house.
The children didn't stir;
her husband slept heavily, ponderous in his snoring.

She felt the thrill of what she was doing.
All alone.
Unknown to everyone around her.
Her secret.
She pulled her shawl tighter,
felt the fluttering giddiness of the enormity that she had chosen.

Supposing she was caught?
She heard a sound behind her and spun around frightened.
It was just a door, creaking slowly in the dim light.
She tried to steady her breathing.
She was breathless, her heart leaping around inside her.
She stood still for a moment,
the blood inside her head thumping in sudden guilt.

Was this worth it?
Every day, as she ran back home,
she vowed this would be the last time.
Every day, as she laboured over the washing of her children's clothes,
she felt consumed with the guilt.
She *would* stop.
She would never go back to the far orchards again.
Every night, as she lit the lamps and listened to her husband's slow talk,
she felt something twist inside her.
Yet every morning,
she woke in feverish excitement.
Every morning she schemed and planned.

Every morning she trod this terrible balance of wanting.
Wanting him.
And wanting it all to go away.

If she was discovered – her stomach turned over.
When you are young and flighty,
death only happens to the old.
Life carries on.

If she was caught . . . But that would be unthinkable.
It simply wouldn't happen to her.
It had happened to a girl in a village ten miles away . . .
But she was stupid, careless.
It wouldn't happen to her.
But if it did . . .

Fear spurred her on.
She ran quicker now,
the houses falling away from her.
She knew the ground well,
which trees to lean on,
which stones to watch out for,
which places to hide if someone chanced to be near.
It was a hard climb but she seemed to be flying,
her feet barely touching the ground.

Was she there first?
She hesitated, another fear suddenly clutching her.
Suppose he did not come today?
Suppose he was unable to get away?
Suppose he was fed up with her,
had had enough of her, was bored by her?
Maybe he had found someone else?

Jealousy, fear, uncertainty, all wrapped themselves into her mind.
She bit her lip anxiously.

Had she risked all – for nothing?
Why wasn't he here? He should be here.
He was always waiting for her.

A figure moved along the path.
She started and stared.
YES! Oh YES! It was him!
She made to run to him but he immediately put a finger to his lips.
She waited fractiously, glancing along the path he had walked.

He reached her a moment later
and she flung her arms around his neck.
"You've come! You've come!" She pressed kisses onto him.
"Shh! I got held up with the old man's donkey cart."
She giggled nervously and held on to him tighter.

He wasn't from the city.
They had met quite by chance, high up in the hills;
he was looking for his father's errant donkey,
she searching for wood further afield from the outskirts of home.
It had been instant.
The furtive glances at each other,
the accidental brushing of fingers
as he helped to straighten her pile of brushwood.
And somehow
it had leaped to this.
Spiralled so rapidly.
All within a matter of days.
A whirling of emotions that engulfed,
consumed her,
creating untold clashes in her mind.
Truth woven through with lies,
deception creeping into everyday living,
justification pierced by the agony of guilt.

They didn't see the man on the brow of the hill;
didn't see him stop and stare.
But they heard the shout,
heard his feet as he ran away,
his cries of alarm sending the birds into the air,
their raucous breaking of the silence
a foreshadowing of what was to come.

The colour dropped from her face,
her hand suspended in mid-air, motionless.

Time stood quite still.
Or maybe it leaped forward.
She seemed already dead.
A ghastly bloodless second self, enclosed and bound by pale death.

Her gaze slowly turned to him for help.
But he was already gone,
getting as far from her as possible,
disappearing out of her life.
Abandoning her.

She was all alone.

A terrific banging of her heart recalled her.
Fear,
the most primeval of all survival instincts, took over.
She raced for the path, lifting her robe,
the trees catching her sleeves, her hair, in the desperate flight.
But she was too late.

Already there were three, four men running towards her,
shouting at her, waving their arms.
She turned and ran through the scree on the hillside,
her feet sliding and slipping,
choking dust rising in great clouds around her.

She was falling, rolling,
the stones tearing her skin, knuckles;
her hands and knees were bleeding.

But still they pursued,
closing in on her, drawing closer.
They could see her face now,
knew who she was.
A pack, moving as one,
tightening for the kill.

She was down the hillside now,
dodging through trees on the edge of the city.
The early morning workers were startled by her,
staring, wondering.
She had no idea where she was going.
Foolishly, stupidly,
she had run for home.
Maybe she could lose them in the twisting warren of streets that she had so nearly reached.
She ran to the very last,
her heart bursting,
her mind bursting.
As they caught her,
flinging her to the ground,
her last sight was of her young children running to her,
their faces screaming with fear,
their young arms reaching out to save her.

Surrounded now by men.
Pushing, shoving, tearing at her.
Ripping her clothing,
her skin,
her hair.
All desperately needing to be part of her death, to destroy her,
to be assured of their own righteousness by being her judgement.

It was all a frantic screaming blur.
She was hurtled onwards,
down streets that she had walked since being a child,
past houses where she knew everyone,
along everything that was familiar and normal.

Except this wasn't normal.
She was racing through a nightmare
of noise and blood and anger and viciousness and fear and shame
and terror.
"O God, have mercy on me.
Have mercy on me," the thought ran round and round
her battered mind.

And then the crowd stopped.
She was pushed forward but could barely stand.
Her head hung low, her hair covering her face.

Strangely,
the noise seemed to slow down.
People stopped shouting,
everything stopped moving around her.
A stillness fell upon the crowd,
as if the madness had temporarily been silenced.
The silence grew.
She knew everyone was staring at her.
Everyone knew her shame now.

Somewhere along the way,
her children had been pulled aside.
In one of the houses
someone else was now holding them,
soothing their hair,
kissing away their tears,
pressing their hands over their ears so they wouldn't hear the screams
as their mother died.

Someone else was keeping them safe.
Another mother.

O God! What had she done?
Forgive me. Forgive me.

The pain was unbearable.
Her heart was breaking.
She was their mother.
She loved them.
They were so little.
So defenceless.
Without her, they would be lost.

O God! Her beautiful, precious children.
Forgive me, God. Forgive me.

She had betrayed the children she had borne.
The pain was terrible.

I am so sorry, Lord. Forgive me.

Somewhere, in the dense crowd of men,
her husband was standing,
his body wracked with pain.
Humiliated and bewildered,
his face crumbling in slow grief.

O God! What had she done?

Why had she not loved him as she ought?
Why had she mocked him through their years of marriage?
Why had she not rejoiced in his steadiness,
in his kindness, in his love for her?
Why had she thrown away their life of struggling together,
for an empty encounter that knew nothing of real love?

O my poor husband! Forgive me.
I am so sorry, Lord.

To betray the trust of the one who loves you is a terrible thing.
Her heart twisted tighter.

O forgive me, Lord.

Somewhere,
hidden behind a house wall,
her own mother was watching,
covering her mouth with her work-worn hands,
rocking back and forth in silent agony,
her heart breaking.

O God! What had she done?

Her mother.
Her truest friend and helper,
who had loved her so completely for all these years.
Her mother, who had been pushed aside for the sake of a man whose name she did not even know,
whose attentions were empty in comparison to the love of a parent.

O my mother!
O forgive me, God. Forgive me!

Somewhere,
not really that long ago,
she saw herself as a girl dancing around a fire
catching the hands of her then new husband,
whilst these people now killing her,
had clapped and laughed and celebrated.

O God! What had she done?

They had been her friends.
They had shared singing and storytelling,
food and news and life together.
Never again.
She had betrayed those friendships
and now they would betray her.
Betray her in death.

O God! Forgive me. Forgive me.

Somewhere, far, far away,
she saw herself as a little girl,
running through fields to welcome her father home.

O God! What had she done?

Her father,
now long dead,
who had adored her,
believed she could do anything, be anything.
She had betrayed his trust in her.

O God – forgive me.
I am so sorry.

She closed her eyes and sobbed uncontrollably.

O God! What have I done?
I have betrayed them all.
O forgive me, Lord. Forgive me.

One of the men stepped forward.
He was speaking now, his voice harsh and eager.
She knew who he was without raising her head – one of the Pharisees.
He was talking to the Teacher, who was visiting.
She thought she knew where the Teacher was.

Just on the edge of her lowered sight,
she could sense he was near, sitting cross-legged on the floor.

She didn't look at him.
There was no point.
Her life was over.
She had thrown away all that was solid and real and good.
So lightly.
Thrown away all the belief and the trust
that comes from years of loving.
Had damaged, so carelessly,
the lives of all who needed her.
Like the seed of a dandelion, thoughtlessly scattered to the wind,
she had ruthlessly and blatantly and wilfully harmed them all.
She didn't care now for herself.
Her thoughts were all caught up in her family,
in the pain she had caused.

Why had she done it?
What had been this madness that had overcome her?
Why had she persisted when she knew it was wrong?
Why had she not listened to her own conscience
that had warned her to stop?
Why, oh why, had she not sought her mother's help?

And she knew,
deep inside,
all the answers.
Because it was exciting,
because it was wonderful to be looked at, admired, wanted,
in a place that did not rank women highly.
And because she had been bored.
Bored with the monotony of the same routines,
the same demands, day after day.
The sameness of it all.

And now she faced death.
And all her reasons seemed so empty,
so shallow,
when laid side by side with the people she loved.

God, have mercy on me I beg.
I am a terrible sinner.
Forgive me
O forgive me, Lord.

"We caught her in the act of adultery."
She flinched at the word.
So ugly. So brutally real.
The voice became cunning, clever.
"Now in the law, Moses commanded us to stone such a woman . . ."
She clutched at her heart. She was going to die. Horribly.
It really was happening. This was real.
"What do you say?" the Pharisee sounded sly, manipulative.

She was going to die.
No one was going to save her.
Never had the ordinary hills, the worn paths of home,
seemed so lovely;
never had the everyday routines and mundane living
seemed so fulfilling, satisfying;
never had she realised
how much of the ordinary could be transformed by living, thinking,
caring beyond herself – as at this moment,
when life was being taken from her.

There was no answer from the Teacher.
But she could see his hand moving,
as if it was writing in the soil.
She moved her lowered eyes fractionally to see more.
The Pharisee was being persistent.
There was an edge in his voice, hard questioning.

Why did the Teacher not reply?
Just say it.
He wasn't afraid of the Pharisee otherwise he
wouldn't be drawing words in the dust.
As if anyone would ever go against Moses' law.

Finally,
she heard the man move,
his hand vanished from the edge of her sight;
she was aware of tiny eddies of dust blowing
across the space between them.
Her head could bend down no further.
The pain inside was killing her.

"Let anyone among you who is without sin,
be the first to throw a stone at her."

The shock held her motionless.
What did he mean?
Was he trying to find out who would throw the first stone?
That was her husband's right, surely?
Was it a clever way of saying, kill her – but don't let the Romans know?
Why didn't he just say, "Stone her?"
What did he mean?

Something was happening around her.
There was more air, as if there was more space.
She could breathe a little easier.
She could see the Pharisee's robes near her –
and then she felt him move.
She tensed in terror.
They were coming to get her!
But he disappeared from her lowered vision.
Where had he gone?
Why was it growing so quiet?

She could sense the presence of people all around her but she could also sense a cool breeze,
as if the men had moved aside.
Were they moving to gather up the stones?
Why didn't the Teacher move away?
The coolness grew.
As did the silence.

The Teacher was sitting again in the dust,
his hand again writing words in the soil.
She could see his feet clearly now.
Her eyes absorbed everything about them,
travelling slowly over his sandals, the worn straps,
the colour, the texture of his skin.

The silence grew.
She could no longer hear the men.
They had ceased shuffling.
The breeze ran across the back of her head.

Forgive me, Lord. Forgive me.

Her heart ached so heavily inside her.
This ending seemed so long.
In a few minutes, it would all be over.

But the Teacher did not stir.
He continued to sit in the dust,
writing words that were swept away by the breeze.
The silence became acute.
How long had she been there?
A minute?
An hour?
A day?
She had no idea.

Slowly she raised her aching head.
Brought her eyes level to the Teacher's shoulders.
Only then did she dare to slide a glance sideways.

She could see no one.
It was an empty space.
She straightened up and stared around her.

They had all gone.
She was utterly alone.
Apart from the Teacher.

She looked fully at him, unable to understand what was happening.
And only then did he move.
He slowly stood up and looked her steadily in the eyes.

She didn't understand.
Had he saved her?
What was happening?
Where had they gone?
Why?
What was she supposed to do now?

The hope of life caught her
and she struggled to breathe.
Her mind went completely blank.

"Woman," he said, glancing around them, "where are they?"

It *was* life!
Being offered her.
He understood!
But how did he know?
Who was he?
What was he?

She stared at him.
For the first time in her life,
when she was facing death and had nothing left to hide
she was aware of the realness of God.

She was being offered a chance to live again.

But.
It was no easy choice.
She had been saved from death
but the alternative was a hard life ahead.
She would always have to remain there,
amongst those people;
she would have to carry the knowledge of her adultery
for the rest of her life;
she would have to slowly try to rebuild the lives
that she had destroyed.
It would be a life-long journey.

"Has no one condemned you?" he asked.
"No one, sir," she replied, almost in disbelief.
"Neither do I condemn you."

She was forgiven.
It was all over.
Her heart pounded inside – but this time it was hope that made her unable to breathe.
Surely only God could forgive?
She looked back at him, puzzled.

God?
He had heard her cries from the depths of her soul.
Could it be that this man…

His eyes never left her.
"From now on, do *not* sin again."
He understood.
And she understood.
Everything was slowly unclouding.
What he was saying
was changing everything.
Taboos, adultery, fidelity,
morality, punishment, atonement – heaven and hell.
Redemption through the overwhelming power of forgiveness.

There was so much turmoiled inside her.
So much she needed to think slowly over.
It wasn't so much about *her* –
but it was *all* to do with God.
Not wrapped up in scrolls and texts,
incanted over by priests and scribes.
This was such a different God.
God of the very ordinariness that made up her life –
amongst these very people and homes that she was a part of.

She couldn't take it all in now.
All she knew was that she was forgiven.
Somehow,
she would be given the strength to live each day as it came.

He smiled at her.
Gently, tenderly.
Full of compassion.
"Go your way."

A new life had been given.
It was up to her what she did with it.

She slowly turned
to face the future.

John 8:1-11

The weight of my wrongdoing is crushing my soul.
I cannot breathe.
I long for my sins to be lifted from me.

O forgive me, Lord.

For the pain,
the causing of grief,
the betrayal of all that is love.

Forgive me, Lord.

I stand hollow in your presence, Christ.
Inward turned
by my guilt.

Why then
do you smile with such love –
and hold your arms so wide, my Lord?

Man of Faith

The room lay dark behind him.
For the moment
his servant slept, fitfully,
the shallow gasps of breath
breaking the weight of the night.

He sank onto the couch,
leaning his head on his hand;
gazed deep into the fire.
Unseeing.
His mind, his heart, aching.

He had paid for the best doctor –
a good man –
knowing he would tell the truth.
The examination had made the servant scream,
his hand reaching to the centurion,
begging him to help.
Afterwards
the doctor had stood in the room,
staring down at the same fire into which the centurion now gazed.
When he had finally looked up,
the centurion knew the worst.
There was nothing he could do.
His blessed friend,
the most trusted of all men,
the servant he loved best of all,
was dying.
He watched a log fall in a shower of rapid sparks.
I can't let him die.
I won't let him die.

The servant moaned
and the centurion moved quietly to be beside him.
He knelt and soothed back the hair from the man's face.
The eyes struggled open.
"Don't leave me," he whispered.

The centurion sat down on the floor,
taking the hot hand in his own.
The servant's chest lifted desperately for breath.
"I'm dying, aren't I?"
The Roman was silent.
There was a hard lump in his throat and the candlelight blurred around him.
The burning hand gripped him fiercely, painfully.
"Save me, Marcus."

Marcus!
The servant hadn't called him by his name since they were children.
Hearing him moan his name in that heavy night,
made the years roll back and they were once again the irresistible,
incorrigible, mischievous boys that had grown up together.
The centurion smiled in the dark.
"You've not called me Marcus in thirty years."
A smile struggled across the servant's face.
"My lord," he whispered.

The centurion slipped an arm under his shoulders
and helped to raise him up so he could drink a little.
The servant's head lolled against him.

Strange.
They had spent their lives together
and yet they had never talked deeply.

Marcus, if he had ever thought about it,
had always assumed that they would, quite simply,
always understand each other,
always be there for each other.
There had been no need for talk.
But now,
when his heart-brother was leaving him,
he discovered that he needed to speak,
needed to pour out his whole being.
A torrent of words that choked him
yet came out unstoppable, unchecked.

He needed to talk about things unsaid –
of how he had loved his servant's mother,
the way she would always include him, when he was a child,
in her embrace;
how he admired, was jealous even, of his servant's skill with horses;
how he had always treasured
the afternoons when the two of them would
disappear to go fishing in the quiet woods;
how he loved to just be with his heart-brother,
sharing the quietness together.
How he was,
completely and utterly,
his very best friend.

He spoke slowly, steadily to him,
knowing that the dying cannot go
whilst their loved ones hold them to life.
But it was the longest time to journey
and the dawn was too far off.
I will not let him die.

His heart poured strength into his servant,
willing him,
commanding him to live.

The servant,
slipping in and out of sick sleep,
woke to find the centurion near;
opened his eyes through the drugged pain
and momentarily focused on the face he trusted;
closed them again
to the sound of his master's voice,
the words flowing around him.
Comforting – sounds, sights, touches of the life
that was closing down on him.

When the dawn finally came,
it was a miserable greyness that surreptitiously
changed night into day.
There were no glorious sunbursts topping the hills
or golden rays that transformed the dying.
It was cold and dreary,
the smell of death cloying the air.

Marcus slowly stood
and straightened his chilled bones.
They had made it through the night,
past the awful half light into a second day.
But he knew in his heart
that his brother would not live to see another night.

He had needed to talk as he had never talked before.
Had needed to pour out the confused thoughts
and half-formed ideas that had never become clarified.
Had needed to sit where no one watched his face
and let his mind unburden.
Those long hours of quiet talk, of tangible speech,
had cleared his mind;
his thoughts now had space to move.
For there is nothing like facing death,
to make life intensely meaningful.

Through those long hours of holding his servant to life,
he had discovered that which he had always longed for.
He had discovered faith.
He knew now that it had always been there.
In his heart.
Simply waiting for him to realize.

For it had been in the dangerous hour –
that shifting landscape before the breaking of the dawn
when the wearied soul is set free –
that Marcus had slowly become aware
that he was not alone.
In the coldness of the dark,
there was the presence of someone else.
Kneeling alongside him.

He left the dying man in the care of his wife
and went to find the Jewish leaders.
They were kind men,
honest and straight forward.
Trying,
like all believers,
to live true to their faith.
He found them at early morning prayers.

He stood away from them to avoid disturbing them.
He would not come between them and God.
He understood.
Grief had opened him in a way that life could not.

When they had finished,
he spoke simply to them.
"I beg you.
Will you go to the man called Jesus and ask him to heal my servant?
As a Gentile I cannot go but…will you intercede for me?"

They liked Marcus.
He had always been respectful of their religion;
keeping his men under strict and fair control.
Unlike some of the Roman officers,
he had earned their respect.

They looked at his tired face
where sorrow sank in worn lines
and nodded to each other.
They had listened many times to the teacher Jesus.
He spoke no heresy –
he preached what was true.
And his gift for healing was doing only good.
Of course, they would approach their fellow Jew.
They were the elders.
He might listen to them.

They moved off as a group,
the people standing back to let them pass.

The waters at Capernaum were always full of the sick;
the elders knew they would find Jesus of Nazareth there,
in the middle of the diseased and dying.

They stood at a distance from him,
unwilling to interrupt his work
until one of his disciples saw them.
He gently touched the arm of the healer.
"We have company from the synagogue," he murmured.

After a moment,
Jesus came to them.
They noticed the wariness in his disciples –
continuing to lay their hands upon the sick
yet very aware of what might be trouble for their leader.

But these older men had come in peace.
The healer instinctively knew that. "What can I do for you?"
They hesitated, and then one of them spoke.
"We have a Roman soldier here,
a centurion,
whose servant is very sick.
We wondered, well, we wondered . . ." he faltered.
"He's a good man. A kind man."
"He has been good to us."
"He is courteous to our faith."
"He helped us build our synagogue."
They looked at Jesus hopefully,
desperately wanting him to say yes,
but acutely aware that they were asking for a man
from the occupying army.
He smiled at their dilemma.
"Of course I will come.
Show me the way."

At the centurion's house,
Marcus continued to kneel beside his servant,
his head bowed,
deep prayer surrounding him.
In the courtyard waited his friends –
Romans –
men he had journeyed with,
fought with,
celebrated with.

Now they came to be with him
as he faced his own grief,
to be one with him.

They noticed the crowd moving up the hillside from Capernaum and
glanced quickly at each other.
"Looks like this healer is going to come."

One of them moved quietly to the darkened room where Marcus
knelt and laid his hand upon the bent shoulder.
Marcus followed him back to the window.
"See.
The man Jesus is coming to you."

Maybe it was because he had struggled with death all night
or maybe it was because he had opened his heart
and laid all that he was before God.
But at the sight of the elders bringing Jesus in their midst,
Marcus caught his breath.
"No! No! He doesn't need to come here.
He cannot.
Not Jesus!"
His friend stared at him, bewildered.
Marcus started to laugh.
"No! No! He mustn't!"
He clutched the man's arms urgently. "I'm not worthy of him. He is…"
His heart told him who the healer was.
He felt terrified yet profoundly moved.
And for a moment,
he remembered the presence in the dark hours.
"Go to him for me.
Tell him that I am a soldier. I understand about obeying orders. I know!
He doesn't need to come here – he has only to say the word –
and all will be well."
His friend slowly nodded and beckoned to the others.
The Roman comrades walked down the hillside
to stop the group approaching.
Even when relaxed they walked like soldiers, with military precision.
A strong group.
Good friends to have.

The Jews stopped, seeing them coming towards them.
"My lord." The Romans were courteous,
bowing to the elders whilst keeping their eyes on this man Jesus.

"We bring a message to you from our friend Marcus, the centurion.
He begs you not to trouble yourself,
for he is not worthy to have you come under his roof.
That is why he did not presume to come to you himself.
But he asks if you but speak the word –
and his servant would be healed."

Everyone went still.
There was an amazed silence around them.
The winds caught the sounds of Capernaum and lightly tossed them on the breeze;
somewhere nearby a dog barked.

The elders glanced in horror at the healer.
Why!
They had brought him nearly to the house.
It was the only way to heal –
he had to put his hands upon the broken body in order to pass the healing through.
Everyone knew this!
What on earth would the man Jesus think?

The Roman continued, unafraid.
"He says that he, Marcus, is also a man under authority, with soldiers under him.
To one he says, 'Go' and he goes,
To another 'Come' and he comes
and to his slave 'Do this' – and it is done."

The Roman stopped.
He had said what Marcus had asked him to say –
no more, no less.
And now he waited for the answer.

The healer seemed as surprised at the others.
Of course he understood.

This was breaking the old law –
the centurion had kept himself and his dying servant away from contact with Jesus –
for he was a Gentile.
Not of Jewish descent.
And yet!
What faith this man had!
He knew he did not need the physical contact.
Jesus had only to say the word
and the centurion believed his servant would be healed.
This was astounding faith!

For a long time
Jesus looked at the Roman friends
whilst his disciples, the elders and the crowd, waited.

The quietness grew as the momentous turning point lay before them.

Finally he turned to the Jewish elders and held out his hands in amazement.
"What faith!
I tell you, not even in Israel,
have I found such faith as this!"
He seemed delighted.
His whole face lit, alive.
He turned back to the Gentiles.
"Go.
Let it be done to him according to his faith!"

They smartly bowed and marched back up the hill.
"Do you think he knows what he's doing?" One of them asked.
"Who? The healer or Marcus?"
The soldier paused, "Well – both of them."
They looked worriedly at each other and bent to enter the home.
They stood in the doorway to Marcus' room.
The curtain had been pulled back and daylight had filtered through.

Marcus was sitting on the bed,
the tears running down his face.
In his arms lay the servant.
Weak and frail.
But the eyes were clear.
"The pain has gone. I'm going to get better," he whispered to the centurion.

Marcus held him tighter, unable to speak,
bowing his head in a prayer of the soul that carried no words.

His companions watched, hesitating to speak.
For words would intrude,
jar on the wonder they were witnessing.
Finally Marcus looked up at them.

He had gone through the most profound of all experiences.
His life –
and that of his household –
would be completely changed by this.

He smiled slowly at them,
for they too had been a part of the extraordinary journey.
"I have found God." He said simply.
"And now living, working, loving-
is different.
I want to live! Grasp at what we've been given and live fully."
He fell silent,
thinking,
then looked up once more,
"And I want to learn more about the healer.
Jesus. He's the one who's changed everything."

And he held his beloved servant closer as life filled the room.

Luke 7:1-10
(Matthew 8:5-13)

O Lord,
Grant me the depth of loving that will
unfold my heart into your presence,
And grant me the depth of faith
to step ever closer
into the wonder of your love.

Called by Name

The house in Damascus was large,
the door wide open in welcome.
Singing rose in small bursts,
laughter drifted on the breeze.
Talking was a contented hum,
the fingers of children interlaced as they wandered and played.

When the two men entered their arrival caused a stir.
"Daniel! You're back! It's Daniel everyone!"
"What are you doing here?"
"We thought you'd gone for the year!"
"What was Jerusalem like? Is it wonderful?"
"Why have you come back so soon?"
"What news have you brought?"
"Did you see them?"

The people crowded round,
greeting, hugging, exclaiming.
The man Daniel tried to respond but over the heads of the people
he caught the leader's eye.
Ananias paused in his smile of welcome.
Something was wrong.
Seriously wrong.
Daniel should not be here.

He waved them down.
"Be seated everyone! Let him speak!"
The crowded courtyard slowly settled,
shufflings and jostlings steadied into listening.

The man Daniel looked ill, grey,
his eyes red and rimmed with sleeplessness.

"My brothers and sisters," he began.
And then his voice cracked –
was it tiredness?
Or was there something else?
Surely,
oh, please, no –
he wasn't going to cry?
The awful stillness of embarrassment caught them.
People looked intently at the floor;
only children stared at him, open-mouthed.

Ananias quietly handed him a cup of water.
Daniel's hand shook when he took it.
He breathed deeply.
"I have seen terrible, terrible things since I left you.
And I have terrible news to tell."
He paused and again, his eyes filled with tears.
"Stephen – is dead."
There was an audible gasp from the people.
"No!"
"How did it happen?"
"Was it the Romans?"
"Why?"
A child leant against her mother. "Who's Stephen?" she whispered.
"One of the men who loved Jesus," her mother whispered back, pulling the child closer to her as if to protect her.

"He was stoned to death – by the council."
A murmur of horror, of disbelief trembled through the listeners.
"Since then, life has become a living hell."
He stopped and pushed the stinging tears from his eyes.
"They come in the early dawn,
smash the door in and take everyone.
The fathers and old men are dragged down the streets,
women beaten, then tied and taken away.
The children are pulled from their parents, kicked to the ground.

All to wipe out our belief in the One."
Someone in the crowd put their head down and sobbed.
"Who is doing this?" asked Ananias. "The Council?"
Daniel nodded.
"They have appointed a young man called Saul.
He's in charge of organizing this hunt."
He looked away as the tears rolled down his face.
"I have seen him.
He is horrific, monstrous, the instigator of violence, like a man possessed.
He will stop at nothing."

The air lay heavy upon them.
The children were still,
gathered close to their parents.
The people were in shock,
numb with the horror that the words had brought.

Ananias looked round.
This lovely, happy, open group –
such a mixture of old and young families;
of the very wealthy and the very poor;
of the illiterate and the learned.
All together.
All one.
This was how the faith had changed them.
And now this beautiful, wondrous belief was being destroyed by the very men who should have embraced it.
Their hearts ached for their brothers and sisters in Jerusalem –
another city, another country –
people they had never met but whom they loved because of the man Jesus.

"There is more." Daniel seemed beyond weary now.
"I've travelled back as fast as I could."
Someone got up and quietly closed the door onto the street.

"The ringleader, this man Saul, has been given letters from the High
Priest asking for aid from the synagogues in his role as a special inquisitor.
He wants to find all who belong to the Way –
and bring them bound to Jerusalem to be imprisoned."
Horror was written over the faces of the people.

"Throughout Palestine?" someone asked.
Daniel shook his head. "The letters are specifically addressed to…"
He faltered, unable to control his breathing.
Ananias went cold.
"The letters are addressed to every synagogue in Damascus.
He'll be here within the day."

—∞—

Ananias shot straight up from his bed.
Sweat was pouring down him; his heart was racing.
He lit the lamp beside his bed to chase the shadows from him.
The light fell upon the sleeping face of his wife –
sleep would bring her no rest, for fear was etched tightly across her.
He bowed his head into his hands,
"Oh Lord Jesus – help us.
Do not abandon us.
Show us what to do."

It had taken the day to sort everyone out.
So many questions. So many unspoken terrors.
A few had openly said farewell – they had relatives in the country
and they could go there for a time –
but the majority had nowhere to go.
When your home is in danger, where do you flee to?
They had talked and talked:
Could they hide?
Where could the children be sent to?
How could they warn each other?
Could they set up watches in the night?
Could they outmanoeuvre the hunt for them?

But, everyone in the synagogues knew them.
They were their friends,
families they had grown up with,
men they had worked with.
These last few months,
as their faith had grown and blossomed,
they had openly shared with their fellow worshippers in the synagogues how they believed that Jesus was the Messiah.
Everyone knew them.
This man Saul would have no trouble in finding them.
Unless they fled, they were all lost.

His head was bursting inside.
All the fears.
The terrors that bound.

"O Jesus help us.
Break the darkness of our fear.
Hold us fast."
He knelt in the room and repeated his prayer over and over in the blackness.
"O Jesus, help us,
O Jesus, help us…"

He was seized in the grip of fear,
paralyzed by it,
knotted into inability by it.
The faces of his children,
his wife, his elderly parents
replayed on his mind.
His heart clenched and plummeted.
He could not save them!

He was their rock,
the master of the house –
and he was powerless to protect them.

Despair crept into his heart,
slowly dragged its emptiness through him,
smothering any flame of courage
with its nothingness.
His hands clenched tighter.
"O my Lord, hear me.
Do not abandon us.
Hold us through the darkness of our fear."

The time seemed to be flying towards the day.
Why was it moving so fast?
A day that would bring such terrors.
His head fell lower
into a fitful half-sleep.

"Ananias!"
He jerked awake.
He knew that voice somehow –
it was as familiar as his father's voice –
but different.
His whole mind leaped alive.
He found he was smiling into the dark.
"Here I am Lord." How did he know?

The fear was gone!
He was simply resting in the beauty of the dark,
surrounded by the presence of God.
All thoughts had vanished,
all terrors
all smothering bleakness.
His mind was not frantically scrabbling.
He was just being.
With God.

He didn't know whether a mere breath had passed
or many hours
or the full night,
when he heard the voice of Jesus again.
"Get up. Go to the street called Straight.
At the house of Judah look for a man of Tarsus
named Saul."

Instantly,
the peace surrounding Ananias broke.
Fear plunged through him,
threatening to burst open his head.

Jesus continued,
"At this moment he is praying.
He has seen in a vision a man called Ananias come in
and lay his hands upon him so that he may regain his sight."

Human fear gripped Ananias so hard
that his chest could not open for air.
"But we have heard of this man – of the …"
he sought the right word,
"the evil he has done to your Saints in Jerusalem. He has come to bind
all those here who invoke your name."

In the midst of the terror that consumed him,
Ananias was sure
that he felt Christ smile.
"Go," said the voice, very gently. "He is an instrument whom I have
chosen to bring my name before Gentiles – and kings –
and before the people of Israel."

The thoughts whirled inside Ananias' head.
Conflicting, confusing.
"I myself will show him how much he must suffer
for the sake of my name."

There was silence –
and stillness.
The struggle between his own knowledge –
and believing the infinite wisdom of God-
slowly subsided.
He had been called.
Of course he would go.

He knelt beside his wife and touched her.
She jumped,
her scared eyes wide in the glooming.
"What is it? Is he coming?"
He caught her hands.
"Don't worry.
We are safe!
I need you to listen."

He told her of his vision.
She sat up,
pushing her hair away,
then brought the lamp closer to study his face.
She nodded "You must go now."
She hurried around the room,
putting his clothes ready,
pushing bread into his hands.
Dawn was breaking –
bringing with it the awful day of dread.

He felt strange.
Purposeful, energised,
knowing what he had to do.
Yet –
walking into the unknown,
not knowing what would happen,
not knowing what he had to say.

As he left,
she caught his arm.
"Oh Ananias – be careful.
It would be so wonderful if..." she didn't finish.
They both knew.
The certainty of faith answering the call.
But the frailty of human nature –
the fears,
the doubts,
the scepticism.
All muddled up together.

He didn't slacken his pace.
He felt somehow that time was important.
He knew Straight Street –
it was the central main road of the city.
And he knew of Judah –
he was a wealthy businessman from one of the other synagogues.
He would easily find the house.

The household was stirring;
the servants preparing the food,
bringing in the water.
He was taken to the master of the house –
they knew each other slightly by sight.
Judah greeted him.
"You have come to see Saul?" he eyed him keenly.
Ananias nodded.
"I think he is expecting you."

A servant took him to the room,
knocked and opened the door for him.
He stepped in,
the door closed behind him
and he was alone with
the Christ-hater.

The windows faced east.
The early sun was streaming through,
catching the dust in the broad beams,
changing the room into a place of light.

Dressed,
standing by the window
was a man.
He was staring at Ananias.
"Ananias?" His voice was low, uncertain.
"Yes."
He stepped forward so he could be seen better
and then realized that the eyes of the man –
open, penetrating, hard –
had not registered.

The man was blind.

"You belong to the Way?"
Ananias felt his heart pound.
At any moment he would be seized!
And then,
at the same instant,
he grew quiet.

This was God's mission!
Why!
God had sent him this far –
it was all exactly as he had been told!
The street, the house, Saul.
He felt like laughing.
He was in God's hands!
He relaxed.
"Yes.
I belong to Jesus," he said quietly.
"Now tell me what happened."

Saul was struggling,
his face mirroring his internal turmoil.
Ananias guessed he was a hard man,
zealous, focused,
narrow,
limited in his vision.
He waited patiently.

Finally Saul spoke.

Ananias was surprised.
There was a charisma, an intellect that was bound up inside the man,
waiting to be released.

But at that moment,
Saul was immensely confused.
Because he was in darkness
he couldn't see what was so obvious to Ananias.

He told Ananias of his role and mission to Damascus.
Then he spoke of a blinding, searing light
that had left him without sight.
And a voice.
A voice calling him, calling his name.
A voice that he now knew to be that of Jesus –
telling him to stop persecuting him.
"And then . . . ?"
"He told me to come here
and await instruction."

For three days he had eaten nothing.
He had drunk nothing
and been able to see nothing.
They had been the most frightening –
and yet illuminating –
days of his life.

Ananias understood.
Saul was in darkness –
and those hours had given him time to think.
About the deepest things in life.
God.
Jesus.
Faith.
The darkness had taught him to listen to the One.

He walked forward and stood before Saul.
Saul didn't move or flinch as he felt his presence so close.
Somewhere,
at the back of his mind
Ananias was surprised –
Saul was a man of courage.
And of faith.

His hands felt they were alive,
sparking within.
He placed them over Saul's brilliant yet dead eyes.
The heat burnt through him,
almost too much to touch.

"Brother Saul," his voice was firm, full of authority.
"The Lord Jesus,
who appeared to you on your way here,
has sent me so that you can regain your sight
and be filled with the Holy Spirit."
He took his hands away
and watched Saul's face.
Slowly he saw the soul-less eyes begin to unmist;
a brightness,
an alertness took over.
He smiled,
seeing Saul scrutinize him.

And then Saul smiled back.
"My brother," said Ananias and wrapped his arms around him.
"You have been enlightened.
It is time for you to discover more of the truth."

Without hesitation,
Ananias offered him his hand.
"Come and live with us.
We will teach you all we know –
and you can teach us all you have discovered."

And so Ananias took Saul to his own home.
Baptized him.
Fed him.
Taught him in words and deeds about the love of Christ.

Thus closed the life of Saul.
And thus began the life of Paul.
The ending of one era –
and the very first steps of the next.

Acts 9:1-20

O God!
How I long to be like Ananias!
To be as perceptive as he
in hearing and recognizing your voice;
to be as courageous as he in listening and obeying;
to be as strong as he in the certainty of his faith.

O God!
How I long to be like Paul!
To experience such an encounter with Jesus,
to know beyond doubt your realness,
to burn with the sole thought of you!

But God,
I am not Ananias or Paul.
I am me.

How amazing that I have been chosen
to answer your call today,
at this time, in this world;
how amazing that I have been chosen
to be faithful and honest and true;
how amazing that I have been chosen
as your light to all peoples.

Grant me grace, Lord –
and help me keep my eyes on Jesus –
as I walk this earth with him.

Amen

The Faithful

The wind was sharp, tasting of the sea.
She would have liked to shelter below deck
but the motion of the boat was turning inside her,
so she stayed in the full force of the buffeting.

At this moment she felt the age of her years.
Her body was cold. Her bones hurt. Her hips ached.
The sky was overcast, threatening rain; the sea, grey and choppy.
The sunlit hallways of home seemed oh, a lifetime away.

She, who had grown up so loved and cherished,
had, as a respected and established woman in her fifties,
been forced to flee her homeland.
These last few years she had been a refugee, in a foreign land.

She looked at her husband, his face turned from the wind.
His hair had gone grey, his face lined with worries and anxieties.
Yet despite the tears from the biting cold,
he had an immense calmness, a serenity about him.
She moved closer to lean against him.

"Despite everything – these last two years have been wonderful," she said.
He followed her eyes to look at their companion.
He was vigorously talking with a group of tradesmen on the boat.
Her husband smiled.
"He is amazing – never missing an opportunity."

Their companion's voice blew back in snatches.
He was quoting scripture –
and suddenly her memory flew back to the time,
nearly two years ago, when she had first heard him.

She had been too far behind the other women to be able to see him.
But she had heard his voice and there was something –
the resonance, a lilt in the nuances – that had caught her attention.

Most weeks, someone new would read the scriptures and preach to them,
certainly during the few weeks that she and her husband had been
establishing themselves in Corinth.
Usually it was men on business, passing through the seaport,
wanting to rest and worship.
She enjoyed the variety.
So many different Jews from so many different countries
brought different ideas and interpretations;
sometimes the preaching would challenge her thinking –
and later, she and Aquila would talk about it
and share their feelings together.

And then the voice had started to read from Isaiah. "Here is my
servant, whom I uphold, my chosen, in whom my soul delights…"
Her heart quickened, she held her breath.
She knew this passage so well!
Her lips formed the words as the reading continued,
"I have put my spirit upon him…"
she could feel her heart thumping inside her.
She knew. She understood these words.
They had taken on a whole new meaning
since she and Aquila had heard about Jesus.
Could it be that this person also believed?
Would he speak about Jesus in this very synagogue?
She could feel the blood rushing to her face.
Oh! Wouldn't it be wonderful!

One of the younger women, seeing her straining to place the new
voice, had kindly moved from the screen to allow her to see.
She smiled her thanks
and pressed her face to the wooden lattice work,
trying to get a view of his face.

He was younger than she had pictured – with an intensity about his whole manner which she could hear in his voice.
"He will not grow faint or be crushed
until he has established justice on the earth;
and the coastlines wait for his teaching…"

That was what they were doing! Waiting. Here, in this thriving, noisy, colourful (but shockingly immoral) seaport – waiting in their hearts.
Longing to hear more of the One,
to learn of His words, to grow in faith.
"O God! Please let this man be a believer -
someone who will feed us, nurture us in the way of Jesus."
The prayer whispered within her soul as she waited for him to finish.
And then he said the words,
"Today – I bring you good news!
Today those scriptures are fulfilled for the Messiah has come!"

She felt she was flying!
She could hardly sit still she was so thrilled!

As soon as worship was over,
she had hurried from the synagogue.
Aquila would bring him back to their home.
She knew he would!
She wanted to be there first, ready and waiting.
She hurried the household into activity,
sending a servant to watch the street.
"He's coming!"
She sat down trying to calm herself but immediately got up again,
nervously smoothing her dress down.
The excitement was almost too much.

Aquila and the stranger had entered through the shop.
She heard him exclaim in delight,
"Oh it's good to be back amongst my trade."
She could hear him picking up the tools.

"They were right to say that you must come to me," her husband's gentle unhurried voice continued their conversation from the street.
"Trade is very busy here."
"Well, I imagine Corinth is a good choice for tentmakers."
She heard the sadness in her husband's voice as he replied,
"We had to leave so quickly – Rome of course will always be our home." And her heart ached.
"But until it is safe to return we must settle here and work hard.
And we could do with skilled help."

She pressed her hands together.
Aquila and this man were getting on so well together!
And the man needed a job!

They came in and Aquila introduced her.
"This is my wife Priscilla. And this is Paul, from Tarsus of Cilicia."

The man glanced warily at her. He had had so much lowness of spirit, so much antagonism in the last few months, that he had resorted back to a wariness when he first met people.

Yet here was love.

He gave a slightly apologetic smile,
"I know my name means 'little' in your language! It befits me – keeps me humble."
She saw all the drive, the energetic force of the man –
and she saw in his face how lonely he was.
She stepped forward and embraced him,
as only a mother could and welcomed him into her family.

How they talked!
Paul telling them again and again of his encounter with the Lord Jesus;
they listening, enthralled, asking questions,
eagerly reading over the scriptures together,
seeing, hearing everything in a new light.

And he worked hard for them, more than earning his wage
whilst explaining to them his mission in life.
"We have such a calling to follow!" he would say, leaning over the low table as they ate,
"It is our *life's* calling! I *have* to preach the Lord Jesus!"

And he **did** preach!
In every place, to every trader, buyer, slave or citizen.
Some listened, some laughed, some mocked.
Many argued. Most berated him.
He was a man who stirred up controversy, anger, unease,
wherever he went.

Several months after he first arrived,
the three of them sat together in the courtyard
at the close of the day's work,
leaning against the warm wall in the last rays of the day's light.
Paul, unusually, was silent.
He had times like this, when everything seemed to be going wrong.
Times when he was tired out with the struggle.

Priscilla took his hand.
"We have a good group meeting here now. It's becoming stronger.
And we are all growing in faith with your teaching."
He tried to smile, knowing that they were trying to encourage him.
"It's not this group I worry about.
This group has you two who hold it together."
They waited for him to continue. After a while Aquila asked gently,
"Is it the synagogue?"
There was a silence. Then an exasperated sigh.
"I've tried so hard to preach within our Jewish faith but..."
"Then you know what you must do." said Aquila.
Paul nodded. "I must preach to the Gentiles."

They sat together, in the peace that comes when you understand each other and there is no need for talk.

"Titius Justus wants me to move into his home and teach them of Christ."
Priscilla straightened up.
"Then you must go!" she exclaimed.

She held his hand firmly. "Of course we will miss you!
But do we not believe in the Christ who calls us to share our faith?
Is that not what you have taught us?
To constantly face new ventures – not to get comfortable in our faith."
"I cause problems wherever I go though."
"No!" she said fiercely. "You make people **think**.
That's what Christ does!
He challenges all our old perceptions and ideas and shakes us up.
It is time now, Paul, to move on. You *must* go to the Gentiles."

"You know, we will always be here." Aquila added.
"Always loving you,
praying for you.
We can't all be Pauls.
We do not have your energy, your fire, your thinking."
Paul smiled at them.
"But you two do have love. Immense love that comes from Christ.
And His compassion. That feeds us all."
Within a few months Paul had needed to move on again.
He wanted to travel to the city of Ephesus in Syria.
The more he talked to them, the greater the conviction grew in
Priscilla and Aquila that they had to go with him.
They knew Paul would not stay long –
and they knew that God was calling them to stay -
to encourage and nurture the seeds that Paul had planted.

—m—

The boat tossed on the currents. She held tightly to its side.
"I do worry about him," she murmured to Aquila.
He nodded.
"That's why we must help him. He has an exceptional gift
– and we must support him.

He can trust us to stay and establish the Lord's work here."
The land was closer now.
Unexpectedly,
Priscilla felt a shiver- not of cold this time but of excitement.
It was unknown.
And there would be immense problems.
But somehow, this was their calling –
and they would do their tiny bit to help in this great vision,
this vast wonderful mission that all believers were being called to.

—∞—

It wasn't easy.
Whereas Corinth had been fraught with immorality and strong individual clashes, Ephesus was fraught with paganism.
Everywhere they went within the city, there were stalls displaying the images of the pagan god Artemis.
Her temple, just outside the city walls, was the pride of Ephesus;
it was meant to be one of the greatest wonders of the world.
All Ephesians purported to belong to her followers.

But Paul was outspoken.
And behind him, quietly and faithfully, Priscilla and Aquila persevered,
establishing their trade yet again, setting up an open home,
enabling and encouraging many to learn about Christ.

And in time, as they had known, Paul had to leave and move on.
His call was to spread the news of Christ as far as he could.
He yearned for Jerusalem –and he yearned to reach Rome,
their own homeland.
But he could leave Ephesus as long as it was in good hands.

And Priscilla and Aquila knew they had to stay.
One day maybe, they would be able to go home
but in the meantime they had to stay in Ephesus.
They weren't called to keep moving,
they were called to stay,

to be the ones left behind.
Often the hardest calling of all.
To work faithfully in the everyday,
through the humdrum of the ordinary, celebrating the high times
and holding fast to Christ through the barren wildernesses.

"These days are hard." said Priscilla one night. "I sometimes wonder – do you really believe that we are making any difference at all?"

She looked at her husband for guidance.
"Well..." he stopped.
He, too, found it very difficult.
"Maybe we simply have to put our faith in Christ like Paul says
and leave the rest in God's hands."

They were wise words.
Comforting.
So they struggled on, trying to teach others
in the ways that they had been taught.
But mostly, trying to show Christ's love through everyday living –
through their praying, their words to others,
their gentleness with each other.

But the times when Paul came back to visit were wonderful!

The three of them sat together one evening after the group had dispersed and gone home.
"You are doing good work here Priscilla." Paul said.

She smiled. He could always read her thoughts.
"Who knows what seeds you have planted or how God will work through them?
Why! Look at Apollos!
You were wonderful with him!
And now he has gone and is travelling all over the land,
proclaiming powerfully, changing many lives.

That came from the work of you two."
"He was an exceptional pupil." Aquila returned.
"But," Paul pointed out, "without you teaching him,
he might never have become what he is."
Priscilla thought over his words.
Apollos had been a lovely man, lit up by his love for Christ but his knowledge of the Lord was very limited. So they had opened their home to him and talked with him over many weeks.
Now he had left and was preaching all over the country.

"We have prayed and thought so long about our work, Paul.
There seems to be such a lot of struggle, for such a lot of the time.
Sometimes we wonder if we make any difference.
We can't be the great thinker that you are,
or the fiery advocate in front of others
or stand up and preach in the synagogue like you.
All we can do is be faithful and true.
And leave the rest in God's hands."

Paul looked up at the growing night sky and thought about what she had said.
No. Not everyone could do what he did.
But then – he couldn't do what they did.
They were all so different yet all working for the glory of God.

How he loved them! This gentle, unassuming, faithful couple.
So kind and patient and full of hope.
Quietly supporting each other, working and loving God's people.
No wonder he loved coming back here – for it was in this home that he found the presence of Christ became real.

"We are all given different gifts.
But you have the greatest gift of all.
That of love."

They fell silent.
The older and the younger.

The tumultuous fire and the calming peace.
The impassioned proclaimer and the quiet faithful.
United by Christ.
The One who was all, in all, to all.

Paul looked steadily at them.
"I do not know if I will see you again."
They understood what he was saying.
His work was dangerous.
Priscilla feared that his life would be lost soon.
He had so many enemies.
How much longer could he keep going,
escaping death so closely each time?
She feared the worst for him.
A burning star that would not last its lifetime.

And what of them?
They were growing older and frailer.
She looked at her husband.
She knew in her heart that soon, one of them would embark on the greatest journey of all – the last and final one – going home to God.
She felt herself fill up with tears at the thought of losing her husband.
And then, she remembered Christ.
And Christ changed death and life.

"Oh but we will meet again!" She smiled.
"When we meet our Lord face to face in heaven.
He holds us here – and will bring us all together again, one day.
And what tales we shall have to share!"

Held by love, the faithful walked on, as they have for generations, with the call of God in their hearts and their eyes filled with the beckoning Christ.

Acts 18 (Romans 16:3-5; 1 Corinthians 16:19; 2 Timothy 4:19)

You are calling, Lord!

You are calling those who are the visionaries,
the ones who can see outside the norm,
to lead us now into a new era.

And You are calling the doers,
the quiet people of faith,
to follow and pray,
to support and nurture.

You are calling the young to give of their energy,
their passion,
their zest for life,
to inspire our way.

You are calling the middle aged,
to make the time,
to keep us focused,
to work tirelessly for you.

And calling the elderly to witness -
in the sharing of their experiences
in the wisdom of their years
in the faithfulness of their prayers.

Christ is beckoning us forward
and the future is in his hands.
Call us on Lord God,
we want to step closer to you.